The Island of Dragons

Less than half a century ago the Komodo dragon lizard was but a "rumor." In 1926, W. Douglas Burden sailed to Komodo Island in the S.S. *Dog* to either dispel the rumor or to capture specimens of the giant lizard. In this true account of Burden's expedition (even the dialogue is based upon written records), the author tells the story of how Burden found and brought back the dragons that are now in the Reptile Hall of the American Museum of Natural History.

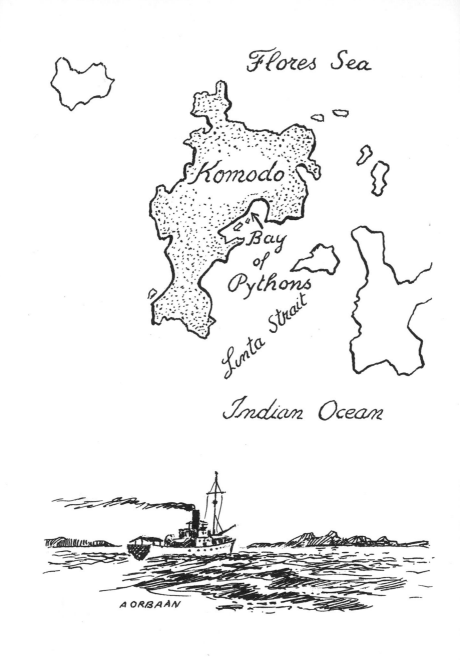

Flores Sea

Komodo

Bay
of
Pythons

Linta Strait

Indian Ocean

A ORBAAN

The Island Of Dragons

By John Clagett

G.P. Putnam's Sons New York

Contents

Foreword

When Americans first stood on the edge of a new continent, they had two choices. They could remain where they had settled and fare reasonably well, or they could journey into a dangerous land, trying through will and initiative to conquer a wilderness. This spirit of adventure built America. In varying degrees, it remains in our people today, for adventure is a natural human craving.

In 1926, a young American heard of strange things concerning a remote spot no white man was said to have visited. His curiosity was aroused. He wanted to see for himself this distant land — this little tide-swept island in a remote archipelago of the East Indies. The urge to go and look and find out for himself was no different from the explorer urge that had animated the early travelers to our Far West. No foundation financed him, no government ordered him, no dreams of wealth lured him. He just wanted to see what lay over the hill. And by doing so he made a myth come true.

The book that follows is the story of that adventure into the unknown. It is true and without exaggeration.

Even the dialogue is taken from records made at the time.

No one guaranteed this young man success or even a safe return. But it was a challenge he could not resist. He had to go. In this book you accompany him on his adventure and experience something long gone in our America of today — the excitement of a new land before you, waiting.

MIDDLEBURY, VERMONT

1

Search for a Dragon

W. Douglas Burden sat quietly in a lecture room in the American Museum of Natural History listening to Dr. G. Kingsley Noble speaking on paleontology — the study of prehistoric animals. Douglas was tense and alert as he listened to what Dr. Noble was saying. His imagination had just taken fire.

The lecturer was just then describing an almost mythical animal called *Varanus komodoensis*. This creature was a giant lizard apparently found only on the small Island of Komodo in the Dutch East Indies. It had never been seen alive by any scientist. T. A. Ouwens, Director of a Museum in Buitenzorg, Java, had written a paper describing a skin brought in to him in 1912. The skin was over nine feet long, and obviously the animal it had clothed was many times heavier than any known lizard. Ouwens was told that the skin was a small specimen and that big ones reached a length of twenty feet.

As Douglas Burden listened to Noble telling of this marvel, his mind was electrified. He had been leading a tame life for many months now. Maybe this would be his chance to get off again to strange seas and unknown lands. What better reason for such an expedition could one ever hope for than the possibility of finding alive and bringing home so strange and so romantic an animal? Dragons had involved the imagination of man from his earliest days, and these lizards or their forebears might be the animals from which the myth had grown.

As Dr. Noble left the subject of the Komodo dragon and went on to other aspects of his lecture, Douglas found his attention wandering to the thought of an animal unchanged from the dawn of time that might be waiting for him on a distant island in the Pacific Ocean.

An uninformed observer might have thought that Douglas Burden was too young and inexperienced to lead such an expedition. His tall, slender body didn't reveal the wiry strength it actually possessed, but a good judge of character might have noticed in his face evidences of the determination he could muster in situations of extreme adversity.

Actually, Douglas had wandered across portions of Alaska, equipped only with a rifle and a piece of canvas under which to sleep at night. He had spent many of his developing years in the Canadian wilderness, which he loved. He had explored in the Himalayas, he had hunted in China, he had spent months in the jungles of southeast Asia. He had hunted tigers, water buffalo, moose, grizzlies, markhor, ibex, and many other animals, less for the thrill of hunting than for the desire to collect for the American Museum of Natural History. He was, at the time of the lecture, the youngest trustee ever to serve in that capacity for the Museum. He was already an experienced adventurer as well as a student of natural history, and there was nothing preposterous about his forming an expedition to search for an almost mythical creature on the distant Island of Komodo.

So it was that Douglas' attention wandered somewhat while Dr. Noble continued his lecture. As he walked home through the deepening winter twilight of Central Park, Douglas' excitement grew. A chickadee swung from a twig and cried cheerily: *spring soon, soon, soon, soon,* not seeming to realize that his age-old prophecy was a little early. Douglas felt spring in his blood, even though it was still winter. Two years had passed since he had been in the jungle, and the long interval quickened his thirst for more adventure. It was time, more than time, to sail again. He walked briskly, the exercise stimulating his thoughts of adventure and travel for a valuable scientific object. It was one thing to go into the wilderness just to wander aimlessly about, and quite another to have an object for the quest that made the whole undertaking worthwhile.

Babs Burden was waiting for him in the apartment that overlooked Central Park. She was a tall, dark-haired girl. Behind her blue eyes existed the inner burning of a search for self-expression that later turned her into an actress on Broadway. Douglas' greeting was nothing less than startling.

"Babs, how would you like to go dragon hunting with me?"

"Dragon hunting? What do you mean? What kind of dragons? What are you talking about anyway?"

Douglas laughed and said, "I mean dragons — the real thing." He was pleased to see in her eyes an enthusiastic response at the prospect of high adventure. So he began to explain the project in greater detail. Naturally, this had been a major question — would his young wife be willing to go? She would! In fact she really wanted to go!

Douglas went to his bookshelves for an atlas and his map case and began studying the Lesser Sunda chain of islands. He read all he could that evening, and on the next day went again to the Museum where he found out more about the rugged and beautiful islands stretching across the Pacific east of Java and south of Borneo. That same morning he wrote a careful letter to Professor

Henry Fairfield Osborn, President of the American Museum of Natural History, outlining his proposed expedition and summarizing some of the very interesting possibilities.

Professor Osborn answered the next day by telephone. He was immediately enthusiastic about the trip. He invited Douglas over for a talk. They discussed the expedition and it was decided that a small group was all that was necessary. Babs could do the still photography, and a movie cameraman could be secured from Pathé News somewhere in the Orient. This was in 1926; the trip would of course be made by ship, and it was only from Singapore that passage could be obtained for Java, which would be the gateway to the Island of Komodo. Douglas would be in command of the expedition. Dr. Noble suggested Dr. E. R. Dunn of Smith College as another member of the group. Dr. Dunn was one of the country's leading herpetologists. The reptiles of the Lesser Sunda chain were little known in the United States, and Dr. Noble — head of the Reptile Department at the Museum — considered it extremely worthwhile that an expert on reptiles should accompany the expedition. Douglas agreed at once, and when he left Professor Osborn's office the Komodo expedition was no longer merely a possible event in the future. It had become a certainty.

Now Douglas had a letter to write that filled him with pleasure. It was addressed to François J. Defosse. Just to write the name evoked many fond memories of the imperturbable hunter who had spent nearly all of his life in the jungles of French Indochina. Defosse was considered the greatest hunter of the entire southeast Asia area, and a man who knew the jungle and its animals as few men ever have. Weeks later came Defosse's reply, saying that he would be glad to investigate, with his old hunting companion, the probably nonexistent dragon that lived, if it lived at all, on a flyspeck of an island in the Pacific. Defosse would, therefore, be in Singapore at the agreed time. Now, with Defosse signed up, there was every reason to believe the expedition would be a success . . . if the lizards actually were there. Defosse could trap any animal that lived, and Douglas had every intention of bringing home some living examples of the species and placing them in the Bronx Zoo as evidence that there was indeed something new under the sun.

There were myriad details to be handled, but the Museum was a powerful ally in making all the final preparations. Moreover, the Honorable Richard Tobin, American Minister to The Hague, and Joseph Grew, Undersecretary of State, interested themselves in the project and worked through diplomatic channels to ensure that the expedition would be welcome in the East

Indies. Guns were checked and put in order. Ammunition was purchased. Cameras were obtained and film specially packed against the heat and humidity of the tropics. Sometimes it seemed as if this business of preparation would never be completed. But at last the departure date arrived.

Douglas and Babs said good-bye to friends and family and boarded not a ship but a train, heading for San Francisco. Dr. Dunn would be leaving New York to travel east, for he would proceed to Batavia by way of the Atlantic, the Mediterranean, and the Indian Ocean. They would meet again in Java.

So the journey to Komodo commenced. After a few days more, and a bad bout of malaria on the transcontinental trip, Douglas at last found his feet on the deck of a ship. He and Babs felt happy as San Francisco slowly merged with the California haze behind them. Now they felt that they were truly started, and their spirits leaped as they looked ahead to the adventures that lay before them.

During the sunny days and star-shot blue nights of the Pacific, Douglas found the dragon lizards and the Island of Komodo constantly on his mind. How would it be? What would the island look like? But he was more than content. Another exciting experience would be encountered before reaching Komodo. From Japan they were going to Peking, China. Dr. Roy Chapman Andrews, a Museum friend and leader of the great Central Asiatic Expedition, had invited him to the Chinese capital. Douglas already knew Peking and was eager to introduce that wondrous city to his wife. This, therefore, was an opportunity not to be missed. But China was in the midst of a civil war, and reaching Peking might be both difficult and dangerous.

After the long passage across the Pacific, Douglas and Babs were happy to reach Japan. Yokohama was still wrecked as a result of the great earthquake, but on the same day they arrived, they went on to Kyoto, the pleasure city of Japan. There they lived in comfort while considering whether or not to go on to Peking before proceeding to Singapore.

Both of them longed to visit Peking, that ancient, fascinating city that relatively few Americans had ever seen. However, the railroad connections between the Port of Tientsin and Peking were cut, and General Chang Sho-lin was advancing on the city, thus blocking all approaches from the sea. In spite of this, Roy Chapman Andrews cabled Douglas in Kyoto that he would meet him in Tientsin and drive him up to Peking by car. Evidently he expected to get through. However, two days later the newspapers headlined heavy fighting on the only connecting road. Peking was being bombed, and food was reported to be scarce. Furthermore, the American Legation renounced all responsibility for Americans traveling in China. Not a very promising prospect, Douglas thought. Alone he would certainly have made the attempt, but with Babs along, it seemed somewhat too hazardous. This was a real war and thousands had already died on either side. Moreover, Chang Sho-lin's Manchus hated foreigners and so the situation could be described as extremely touchy.

Douglas cabled Andrews once more: SHOULD WE COME? Andrews sent back one word: COME.

Douglas wasn't surprised. He knew Andrews well and he also knew something of the frame of mind of those who lived in Peking. They took for granted dangers and difficulties that people living in security would do everything to avoid. Douglas believed, as he said to Babs, that there would be plenty of time in later life to be careful and to play safe. But right now seemed a time for living positively. He said, "Let's go." They boarded a dirty Japanese freighter, the *Chosa Maru*, and sailed down the inland sea toward China.

This was a strange way to reach Komodo and the dragon lizards, but Douglas was unwilling to forego the opportunity for adventure. He was most anxious to see Peking a second time and to learn from Roy at first hand about his recent discoveries in the Gobi Desert that had enthralled the scientific world. Nor was China unconnected with his quest. Douglas was convinced that if the Komodo lizard existed at all, it must have originally been prevalent on the mainland of Australia, and might even have lived in China. Perhaps their fossil remains would some day be found in the Gobi Desert. He was most anxious to show that earlier forms of these lizards had coexisted over wide areas with man, and China seemed to offer such a possibility, for China had always been greatly concerned with dragon mythology.

China loomed before them. The *Chosa Maru* puffed wearily upriver to a crowded dock, and the smell of the ancient land came across to Babs and Douglas as they stood on the deck, watching the jostling, crying, shouting mass of humanity ashore.

"Now for Roy and Peking," he said hopefully. Babs looked a little comforted, and they went back to their cabin to oversee the transport of their baggage.

2

The Dragon of China

Unfortunately, when the Burdens went ashore there was no Roy Chapman Andrews. All communication with Peking had been cut off and there was no way by which Roy could reach Douglas or Douglas reach Roy. The gates of Peking were closed and sandbagged, and fighting at the moment was in progress near Tungchow about twenty miles outside of the Imperial City. There was no prospect at all of reaching it in the near future. However, in the lobby of the hotel Douglas fell into the lap of good luck.

There he ran into an American named McCann whose wife was seriously ill in the hospital in Peking. McCann informed Douglas that he was leaving for Peking in half an hour by car. He was going to do his best to get through. He would give the Burdens passage if they were willing to risk it. Douglas soon learned that McCann was an old China hand who spoke Chinese perfectly and knew the Chinese people well. He was an excellent mechanic as well as driver. Such an opportunity was not to be lost. He found Babs and said, "We are off." By two o'clock they were on their way, racing through the streets of Tientsin with the horn blaring every minute. It was a ride Douglas and Babs were never to forget.

The road was filled with refugees pushing away from the war and toward Tientsin. They blocked the road, they held back the car, they cursed and shook clenched fists at the foreign devils in the automobile. As they traveled, Douglas and Babs saw alongside the road the graves of past centuries, heaps of earth piled in pyramid fashion, varying in height according to the dignity of the man or woman buried there. The fields were nearly deserted, for all the young men had been conscripted into the armies. A few old men were out plowing. Some carried the ropes over their shoulders and pulled while their wives directed the plow, for all oxen and horses had been taken by the soldiers. But these people knew that unplowed fields meant starvation during the coming winter.

At one point officers of General Chang's rear guard stopped the party and demanded passes. McCann asked Babs if she had calling cards. She handed him several, and he passed them over, telling the Chinese officer that they were safe conducts from the generalissimo himself. Douglas held his breath, but the officers saluted and let the car drive ahead. The car moved past gun emplacements, trenches, and machine gun posts, shuddering and crunching over the difficult road. Then the party discovered a Chinese general in a car that had broken down. They offered him a ride, and it was only later that they found he was the head of General Chang's air force and therefore a person of consequence and authority. In spite of this incredible good fortune, many difficulties were yet before them. The car caught fire! The passengers leaped out and extinguished the blaze by throwing dirt on it. McCann managed to make repairs and they went on. Late in the evening they arrived at Tungchow, where the heavy fighting of the day had been reported. Reports were true. During that one day, Tungchow had been reduced from a prosperous city to a wreckage of bricks and miserable people. Dust and smoke hung over the place like a cloud. But the American mission stood, a sanctuary untouched and alone in the midst of ruin. They drove into the courtyard. The missionaries persuaded Douglas that he should leave his wife there. They assured him that no man could get through to Peking. McCann, Douglas, and the Chinese general sped on in the car, Douglas with the bitter and growing realization that he should never have left his wife, no matter how good the motives. Nevertheless, she would certainly be safe in the mission.

Then as they advanced through the center of the invading army, horses and mules were frightened by the car and its horn; they reared and broke loose, galloping away with carts and guns. The soldiers spat curses at the foreign devils. The noise of the car spread pandemonium among the wild Manchu horses. The troops were furious, and small wonder. The soldiers handled their rifles, bayonets fixed, in a most menacing manner. When they became too vehement, General Chow put his head out of the window and gave a few sharp orders that worked for that moment. However, just after sunset, the great walls, battlements, and watchtowers of the Chinese capital showed up black against the sky. The Eastern Gate, itself a great fortress, stood before them, towering from the plain against the golden sunset.

They passed severed heads hanging from the branches of trees and threaded their way through the troops and animals, always creating more havoc. At last they drew up under the shadow of the Eastern Gate. The two gigantic, nail-studded doors were closed and bolted, with sandbags against them on the inner side. General Chow stepped from the car, walked up to the gate, and shouted. A sliding panel opened and he shoved papers inside.

After a long, tense wait, he came back to his seat in the car. "It's all right," he said in Chinese, translated by Mc-Cann. "They are opening the gate. I am expected. I am to be in charge of Peking."

So it was that Roy Chapman Andrews, after having tried for two days in vain to have the gate opened, and who was at that very moment standing frustrated before it after another unsuccessful attempt at bribery, was ordered by the guard to stand aside because an important party was coming through. Andrews watched and saw the gates open, a car lurch into the city. He looked again in astonishment and saw Douglas Burden in the back seat of the machine.

Douglas spent a physically luxurious night, but he was tormented with concern for Babs. The next day he, McCann, and Roy took the trip back to Tungchow to pick her up. They had to talk their way past the executioners. One gigantic barbarian, waving an immense double-handled sword, acted as if he wanted to drag them from the car and decapitate them on the spot. McCann joked with him, took the sword from his hand, admired it, and spoke aloud in Chinese about the efficiency of the weapon and of the fine purpose it served. He handed it back to its owner along with a few coins, and the executioner cleared the way for them through the mob of soldiers.

Babs had spent a miserable night, worried for herself, worried about Douglas, and haunted by the sad austere life of the missionaries. She was sickened by the cowering hundreds of Chinese women and children who packed the very basements of the mission, lying one on top of another, many of them not having had any food in days. Through an open door, she saw with delight the car come into the compound. She ran from the mission house, almost forgetting to thank her hosts, and leaped into the car which started back immediately for Peking. General Chow, their passenger of the day before, had given Douglas a red strip of paper about ten feet long. It was a strongly worded document allowing passage through the troops, and they reached Peking safely. The executioner had been at work and fresh heads were displayed hanging by the hair from poles. It was a savage sight. Douglas doubted that even the dragon lizards of Komodo could be as cruel and remorseless as the human dragons of China.

Unfortunately, more fighting had started in the north and Douglas and Babs were unable to go to the Gobi Desert. But they were recompensed to some degree by the fascinating two weeks they spent in the Imperial City. They lived the life of Chinese royalty in earlier centuries. In the European colony, social life proceeded normally, including polo and horseracing.

Since things immediately around Peking had quieted down, Douglas and Babs were able to go to the Black Dragon pool, a temple hidden in the western hills, riding there in sedan chairs carried by four men. The very name of the temple brought forth more discussion of the importance of the dragon myth in China's history and culture, and caused them to speculate again as to the origin of the worldwide dragon motif.

Merchants came to the expedition compound in Peking and offered for sale rare fabrics and works of art, some of them thousands of years old, the products of patient and skillful work of Chinese craftsmen over the centuries. At the Winter Palace they attended a dinner of a hundred courses in the old Chinese style, cooked by the Emperor's cooks, served by his servants. After such delicacies as shark fin soup, birds' nests, fish lips, duck tongues, plus scores of others unnamed and unguessed, they stepped into a great canopied marble barge strung with lanterns, and fixed stationary on the moonlit water.

On previous trips to the Orient, Douglas had been fortunate enough to secure the services and loyalty of a Chinese servant of the highest type. Chu had been with him in Mongolia, the Philippines, and the jungles of Indochina. The marvelous Chinese grapevine operated, somehow, and Chu turned up in Peking, looking for Douglas. Nothing could have been more welcome.

Looking at Chu's happy smile of welcome and snapping dark eyes, Douglas felt that no better omen for the success and comfort of the next months could have been secured. He knew that he and Babs need no longer worry about details. Chu would take care of their clothes, their baggage, reservations, hotels, food, everything. Life would be luxurious and pleasant at all hours of the day and night with Chu around.

When the two weeks were over and it was time to leave for Komodo, Douglas and Babs motored back to Tientsin. The area was now firmly in Chow's hands, and nothing worth relating occurred on the trip that had been so hair-raising only two weeks earlier. Roy Chapman Andrews drove down with them and, early in May, they said good-bye to him and boarded the SS *Tungchow*, bound for Shanghai. Douglas retained a pair of revolvers in his cabin luggage, just in case. On her previous voyage, the steamer had been captured by Chinese pirates. They killed the officers and looted the first-class passengers. Afterward they abandoned the vessel near a small town called Swatow. Such piracies were then frequent in the China Sea. The pirates would come aboard disguised as peaceful Chinese passengers, smuggling in weapons under women's skirts, or concealed carefully in their belongings. They struck in the middle of the night at a prearranged moment, an attack very difficult to prevent or even to guard against.

The trip to Shanghai was not a relaxing one. The ship was uncomfortable, the weather rough, and the bandit threat did not add to their peace of mind. However, the Burdens arrived safely at Shanghai and departed from there by the American liner *President Polk* for Singapore, going by way of Hong Kong and Manila.

Douglas was very glad to leave the ship in Singapore, for the great adventure was drawing closer. They took rooms at the famous Raffles Hotel, scene of a thousand romantic tales of the East. Within an hour a note arrived. Douglas read it with pleasure, for Defosse was waiting for him in the lobby below. Douglas hurried down and quickly found the powerful, leather-faced man, still dressed in faded blue coolie-cloth hunting clothes. He had deepset dark eyes with fire in them; he had a small mustache, and a horny, heartwarming grip. His somber face broke into a smile of pleasure and welcome. He had been feeling very sorry for himself, he explained, because he was in such civilized surroundings. He had not left his jungles in Indochina for twenty-four years. Old times surged back into Douglas' memory as he talked with François, and new confidence for the expedition came to him. Defosse was an excellent hunter and woodsman. He was not a man to take fright, and he knew the animals of the jungle and their ways as well as any man alive.

Douglas had often wondered at Defosse, especially at his willingness to bury himself in the wilderness for his entire life. He was courageous, honest, truthful, and a keen observer; an ideal companion for an expedition to dangerous places. He was well read, an excellent linguist, and a man of unusual intelligence. He had written articles for the *Atlantic Monthly*. Douglas thought to himself that his only weakness was a trait caused by years of self-dependence in the jungles. He was too self-willed to accommodate himself comfortably to a new environment. In Singapore, he suffered agonies. He was out of his element with the crowds of people. He was frightened at the prospect of seasickness. Douglas asked him why he was still wearing his hunting outfit and he said, "They are men's clothes." Always his thoughts were back with his family in the jungle, his Indochinese wife and his children, particularly one of his sons who was a hunter and a chip off the old block.

Also in Singapore, Douglas secured the services, from Pathé Frères, of a Chinese moving picture photographer by the name of Lee Fai. Lee Fai could handle a camera and knew something of photography, but his imagination did not stray very far. He hated to expend physical energy. He believed in the philosophy of least effort. But he was good-natured, cheerful, and quiet. He thus endeared himself to Babs and Douglas during the strenuous days of the trip though his ambition as a cameraman left something to be desired.

With his party complete, except for Dunn who would join them in Java, Douglas and his companions sailed in a Dutch liner for Batavia. When they arrived after an uneventful but beautiful voyage, it was found that the Dutch authorities in the East Indies had declared Komodo a game preserve and no one was allowed to hunt or capture the dragon lizards. Douglas was dismayed until he remembered his diplomatic contacts and went to the Governor General himself. He was not disappointed. Not only was he given permission to capture lizards alive and shoot others as scientific specimens, but through the generosity of the Dutch Government, he was also supplied with a ship, the SS *Dog*, a seaworthy and well-equipped small vessel. She was not exactly a yacht, but she was perfectly capable of carrying the party to Komodo and of taking them away again, afterward.

From Batavia, the expedition proceeded in the *Dog* to Surabaya, and sailed from that place on Friday, June 4, 1926, for Bima. The Straits of Madura were calm, the air was cool and pleasant, and the first dinner aboard

The S.S. *Dog*, when not at sea, still showed much evidence of being a floating home.

was excellent. Douglas was supremely happy. After all difficulties, he was on the final stage. On the second night of the voyage as she passed through Alas Straits, the *Dog* moved into a heavy tropical storm. Black seas pounded over the bow during the night and poured around the decks with a howl of wind and a roar of waters. The smashing seas made the whole ship shudder through and through, and Babs found that her head was splitting with the thunderous tumult and violent motion. Defosse was miserably seasick, as he had feared, and lay in his bunk longing to be back in the jungle with a man-eating tiger to deal with instead of an ocean storm. The *Dog* was being unmercifully battered, and the storm became so violent that at two in the morning Douglas went up to the bridge to see how things were going. He found the master of the ship calmly reading a novel. He had ordered reduced speed, and was content to let the ship wallow in the high seas. They were in no danger, the captain said, but the storm was indeed a heavy one.

The expedition stopped briefly at Bima, where Douglas took his letters to the Resident Commissioner and the local Rajah. He was able to secure the assistance of Malay hunters and porters for the duration of the expedition, sixteen strong and experienced men. Douglas found the Assistant Resident a very interesting and helpful man who knew something about the dragon lizards.

Now one last day's voyage and Komodo would lie before them. The *Dog* would have to navigate through foaming tide rips, heavy swirling currents, and treacherous reefs to Telok Sawa, Python Bay, an anchorage on the eastern end of Komodo. The great adventure on the mysterious Island of Dragons was about to begin.

3

Landfall

Douglas Burden walked to the port wing of the bridge and leaned on the canvas windshield. Far ahead, mountains rose above the brilliant sea. Although he was tired of the SS *Dog*, it was not merely the thought of leaving the little ship that made him eager and impatient. Those mountains were on the Island of Komodo, the place he had traveled more than fifteen thousand miles to reach.

Dragon lizards. Did they still exist? Were they really to be found? Great beasts twenty to thirty feet long had been reported by wandering natives, but surely these reports were grossly exaggerated. Douglas thought hard about the chances. He was impatient to learn the truth.

As Burden paced the bridge, the captain watched him curiously — when he could take his eyes from the reefs, rocks and tide rips that lay all about. This was a dangerous area. The waters of the Flores Sea were driven through this narrow passage into the Indian Ocean by the constant monsoon winds, and created currents up to thirteen knots that swirled and foamed over the countless shoals and reefs of coral.

But Burden seemed to be enjoying the excitement. The captain had told him what he might expect to find on Komodo: every variety of deadly snake and insect, crocodiles and, if they existed, the dragon lizards. The captain shook his head. The more he spoke of such things, the more keen this young American seemed to become.

A spare-looking youngster, the captain thought. Tall,

Douglas Burden as he looked on the Island of Komodo.

dark-haired, burned brown by outdoor life, cheerful, not careless but seemingly carefree in spite of previous experiences with tropical diseases — malignant malaria and amoebic dysentery.

There — another reef, with the current piling white water around it. A clear sea to starboard, and the chart showed plenty of water there. He'd bring her right a little.

Douglas looked around at the sound of voices and saw Babs with François Defosse and Dr. Dunn. They were talking excitedly among themselves, discussing, he knew, the same island that was the center of his thoughts and which now was growing ever larger in their sight. Dr. Dunn looked the tall, suntanned, middle-aged college professor that he was. Defosse contrasted sharply with the American professor. He was short and rangy and thin, ridden with malaria but wiry and strong. He smiled quietly at Babs and was entertained by Douglas' enthusiasm. Somber stores of experience lay behind his eyes. When Douglas told him that the captain expected to anchor very soon, Defosse shrugged. Then he unbuttoned his left shirt pocket and took out a heavy silver watch that was connected to another object hidden in the other shirt pocket by a plaited leather thong. He looked at the watch, then at the sun. In answer to everyone's excited wish to go ashore as soon as the ship anchored, he agreed that it would be nice to stretch the legs and get a little feel of the island before dark.

As the SS *Dog* entered Linta Straits she began to pitch and roll, not with the regularity caused by big ocean swells but tossed as if she were a chip in a caldron of boiling water. The sea boiled and seethed. When he saw these currents, Douglas understood why no sailing ship had ever visited Komodo in the early explorations of the area. Wallace, the great explorer and naturalist, had once sailed through the straits here. He wrote that vessels were swept about helpless in these waters, and sometimes swamped in the finest weather and under brightest skies. Douglas could well believe it.

Within an hour, Komodo's mountains were closely visible, rising from a sea of all shades of blue and green, and ringed with the white froth of the currents. Komodo glowed with many beautiful colors in the shifting light. Douglas found excitement growing within him. It was a volcanic island with high peaks, studded with strange-looking basalt plugs that marked ancient volcanoes. From the valleys these plugs jutted into the sky like enormous teeth. Weird-looking palms, some of them of tremendous height, grew above the beaches. The mountains were blue and gnarled, and the sun looked golden on them. It was like an enormous, weird garden.

After so many days of waiting, the hour of arrival

A close-up view of the terrain on Komodo. Note the tall palm trees.

had finally come and the thought of what might live in this wonderful-looking island filled Douglas Burden with delight. He knew jungles and wild places. He had good weapons, and Defosse was a great hunter who could be depended upon in any emergency. After all, this was a man with 98 elephant and 45 tiger notches on his gun. Dr. Dunn was an old campaigner, and they had some good men with them who seemed eager for anything. As for the lizards or whatever they found ashore — well, it was fun for Burden to speculate. He had hunted in many lands and under every condition. He had shot many species of dangerous game. All he really was concerned about was whether the dragon lizards, *Varanus komodoensis*, would really be there, and would be big enough to constitute a significant discovery.

The jagged peaks stretched up to varying heights above the ship as she drew closer to the coast. Mountains within the island were blue, those closer to the shore showed black rock above the covering of tropical growth. As the vessel moved along, he could see into the mouth of each valley, a green sunshine-gilded place of mystery. Then the valley would shut itself off, only to have another one open up. Once the ship turned nearly halfway around in a vicious surge of current, and she came so close to a reef that all the passengers felt uneasy. As the best anchorage, the captain had selected Python Bay. The bay was sheltered and contained a small island behind which the ship could anchor in perfectly calm water.

In midafternoon the SS *Dog* entered Telok Sawa, the Bay of Pythons, and steamed with her engines turning more and more slowly toward the small island that lay a few hundred yards from the shore. A bell jangled on the bridge. The captain shouted down a voice pipe. The engines stopped, and the ship glided slowly through the water. The captain shouted again, the mate on the forecastle waved his cap, and the anchor splashed over the side. The ship vibrated and rumbled as the chain ran out. Then everything was silent, and the ship drifted around and became steady and unmoving. The captain smiled with satisfaction.

He looked surprised when Burden asked that a boat be put in the water to take the explorers ashore. But he shrugged and blew his whistle. His orders sent several of the crew to work and in a few minutes the smallest boat aboard was bobbing in the calm water alongside. Douglas, Babs, Defosse, and Dr. Dunn climbed down into it. Two Malay oarsmen grinned cheerfully at the foreigners and began to row for the nearby shore.

Everybody was fascinated by the land ahead. The poignant smell of a tropical island drifted more strongly to them as the oarsmen pulled steadily for the beach — a smell made up of flowers, growing things, fruit, salt water, tidal flats — a sweet, wild perfume that will haunt a man all his life if he once smells it. In this quiet bay there was little surf, and within a few minutes the bow of the whaleboat crunched on the coral sand. The Malays went overboard, their bare copper legs glistening in the water. They hauled the boat farther in. Burden climbed over the bow and helped the others ashore. The beach of Komodo felt good under their feet. For a moment they stood listening.

A bird called from within a patch of jungle. Far off another bird answered. Something rustled in the tall grass. The air was cool and exhilarating. The sailors hauled the empty boat well up on the beach. Then all six of them stood in a little group by the bow, looking up at the island. A flight of yellow-crested cockatoos flew directly overhead, screaming harshly at sight of the intruders. A dove called softly from down the beach. Babs noticed some tracks in the sand and Defosse identified them as those of deer and wild boar. There would be plenty of fresh meat for the killing here, and plenty of carcasses to use as bait for the carnivorous lizards.

To move again was wonderful. To have unlimited space instead of the cluttered area of the little ship's decks was a relief for all. Babs and Douglas walked together ahead. Sometimes he forgot she was there as he looked up at the mountains or at the patches of jungle, all covered by the reddening light of the sinking sun. They walked for miles. The mystery of this untram-

Another view of the Komodo terrain, with a member of the expedition in the foreground.

meled island pulled like a great magnet. In this new place, unscarred by man, the animals and reptiles lived as they had lived through the ages, a picture in miniature of the world as it had been before man appeared. Burden was inexpressibly happy.

Sunset was painting the sea, the bay, the little island, and the mountain peaks behind them in soft, shifting colors as the party returned to the ship. The captain welcomed them aboard.

Burden and his wife slept on cots on the bridge that

night. The stars were like small distant searchlights in the black sky, and a thin new moon arose. As darkness gathered, drums began sounding from across the bay. An island boat, a proa, had been swept into the bay by the current, and now her crew was drumming for a wind to take her out again. With the high peaks of Komodo against the stars, and the weird, rhythmic pounding of the drums overlying the distant sound of surf, Douglas and Babs had trouble going to sleep. Tomorrow would be a long and exciting day. Burden tried to calm his excitement and lay very still, thinking of many things. At last he drifted off.

When Douglas awoke the next morning, he was filled with anticipation for whatever might lie ahead. The tropic morning was cool and fresh with dawn, the high mountains just coloring with the sun. The sea breeze blew, bringing with it the smell of the ocean, turning the SS *Dog* around until her bow pointed straight out to sea. Burden, Dunn, Defosse, and Babs had a quick breakfast together on the afterdeck. It was decided that Babs would stay aboard that day. The men wanted to find a spot for a permanent camp ashore, and that meant rough going. Dr. Dunn and Defosse were to head north along the coast while Burden struck out due west over the mountains with two of the Malays. Both parties would hunt for water and a place for the base camp.

Though the sun wasn't high, the morning was hot by the time Douglas and the Malays started up the blackened mountainside. They had to push their way through tangled saw grass that cut like jagged razors. Loose lava boulders with knifelike edges rolled underfoot as they climbed. Saw grass and sharp stones worked their will on Burden's boots and clothes during the long climb. Several hours passed before he and his companions reached the plateau that overhung Python Bay.

Douglas paused in pleased surprise. The flat area before him was like a jungle-studded park, rolling and beautiful. A cool breeze came from somewhere, refreshing as a swim in a Vermont mountain stream. The sudden transition from blackened lava and heat to a luxuriant and beautiful world was delightful. Burden heard the sound of jungle fowl that he had met in the jungles of Indochina; he saw blue pheasants and several species of pigeons, turtle doves, and quail. The cockatoos resented the presence of the strangers and kept flying overhead, squawking raucously.

"*Tuan,*" said one of the Malays, pointing. Beyond the bamboo, a wild boar trotted past, paying them no heed. Burden saw a herd of deer feeding on a distant mountain slope. This was a real paradise!

The Malays urged Burden to shoot a deer, but he shook his head. They had not yet found water and a place to camp. When that was done then he would get some fresh meat.

The party moved on through the patches of bamboo, deep jungle, and open grassland. Burden's boots had been so badly cut during the climb over the lava rocks that the soles flapped dismally with every step and his hands and wrists smarted from the saw grass cuts. However, he was happy and elated. Anything could happen on this island — anything could be here. Presently one of his men pointed and grunted in pleasure.

"Look, *Tuan*, water!" he said in Malay.

The small pool in the rocks glinted in the sun, its water clear and inviting. Douglas' thirst redoubled at the sight, but now it was a sensation of pleasure, not discomfort, with cool water only yards away. The natives ran forward and lay on the black rock side by side to dip water to their mouths and faces with cupped hands.

Burden sat down with a sigh of relief and pleasure. A breeze ruffled his hair, released from the sun helmet, and cooled his wet face and hands. The view was superb, the air fresh, the water sweet and good. Here was an ideal place for a camp — water, wood, game, and maybe . . .

Then he suddenly noticed something that made him exclaim, "By George, look at that!"

Over across the pool on a muddy stretch of ground

Tracks of the dragon lizard. Note the drag mark of the heavy tail, most obvious between the footprints.

was a series of tracks. Burden went over to study them. They looked like the tracks of large, heavy birds, sunk deeply in the mud. Between them ran a heavy meandering line. The whole thing reminded him of the grape leaf and vine motif he had seen in decorations. Something big had walked here dragging a heavy tail.

"A dragon lizard!" Burden said aloud. The Malays looked silently. Burden felt an outpouring of delight. This expedition was not to be a wild-goose chase, as some had predicted. He shifted the Lebel rifle to his right hand. He didn't think the lizards would be dangerous, but no one really knew. He walked cautiously as he led the two natives into a patch of jungle.

In fifty yards, they came upon something that stopped Douglas cold. Tracks like those of a large bull were deeply indented across their path. He brought in his breath, held it, expelled it in a sigh, feeling his pockets for spare cartridges. The Malays were studying the tracks.

"Carabao," said one of them.

"Yes." The Malays didn't seem too frightened, but Burden was uneasy. Experts classified the water buffalo as more dangerous than a tiger; a water buffalo has been seen to kill a tiger in a fight. And certain individuals were irascible, ready to charge at sight if the mood was upon them. Burden was glad that the Malays seemed unconcerned, but they didn't know that he had only lead bullets with him. Lead missiles would merely richochet off the tough hide of the water buffalo. Warily he led on through the jungle, following the buffalo tracks. They were not too fresh, and he certainly would rather go where the animals had been earlier and so not blunder on a herd in the forest.

Deer tracks were everywhere, and Burden sighted several more of the animals. "*Tuan*," said one of the Malays wistfully, "*pasang rusa.* [Master, please shoot a deer.]" Burden nodded. He too would like some fresh meat after the canned beef of the SS Dog. A little farther on he sighted a big buck and dropped him with a single shot at two hundred yards. The Malays were much impressed. Their faces were one broad smile as they watched the animal fall and lie motionless. But while the blast of the shot was still echoing from the mountain, the sound of violent crashing came to them from a nearby patch of jungle. Fortunately the sound — therefore the animal that made it — was receding. Burden knew it of old. A water buffalo startled by this totally new sound on Komodo — the crack of a rifle — was making off through the jungle growth.

While the Malays were cutting up the deer, Burden climbed the last long stretch that separated him from the summit ridge. When he gained it, he stood entranced by the wonderful view. The island, the sea, the sky, were revealed in a warm, clear light that brought out all the colors of rock and jungle, beach and ocean, the shading of the water from light gray in the shallows to deep blue in the depths. Sunshine sparkled, a cool breeze refreshed him. He had never been happier in his life.

Then on a distant hillside a large dark object moving in the grass caught his eye. His breath stopped. He lifted his field glasses.

It was a giant lizard, a large one! The sight took his breath; it required all his self-control to hold the glasses steady so he could see. The lizard was striding rapidly down the grassy slope. He was a good half mile away but he looked enormous. A black shadow preceded the animal as he moved. As Burden watched, the lizard stood up on his hind legs, balancing against his tail, like paintings of dinosaurs he had so often seen. The lizard swung his ugly black head to and fro, obviously hunting for game. He seemed to belong to these black rocks and this weird island with its strange pinnacle formations and unearthly vegetation. Burden watched, filled with excitement, for he felt he must surely be the first white man to set eyes on a dragon lizard.

The giant reptile dropped on all fours again, paused a moment longer, and disappeared in a patch of jungle. Burden shook himself, picked up his rifle, and made his way silently back to where the natives had built a fire, offering, in their human company, a return from a vision of the ages long since gone.

4

Buffalo

Douglas had been very tired from the tough climb, and the sun on the lava hillsides had given him a headache. The excitement and exhilaration of the sight of the first dragon lizard had driven fatigue away but now it returned and he was quite satisfied to say yes when his companions indicated that they would like to cook and eat some venison before starting the long trek back to the ship. He could rest a bit, and certainly something to eat would revive his strength.

Douglas sat in the grass and leaned his back against a rough lava boulder. He closed his eyes, hearing the soft chatter of the two Malays, the sighing of the wind in the bamboo thicket, and the liquid calling of birds, increasing now as the afternoon waned. A jungle cock crowed, doves called mournfully, and several of the great yellow-crested cockatoos made metallic noises in the distance. Smoke from the fire blew across him; it smelled much the same as wood fires in the Adirondacks, and now a pleasant odor of cooking meat came with it. He opened his eyes to see that the Malays had impaled strips of venison on green bamboo shoots and were cooking them over the fire. The smoke eddied in the breeze and made a pale net against the yellow and green vertical stripes of the bamboo grove. Douglas was very content. This was the life he desired above all others.

His rifle was leaning against a rock some ten feet away, and Douglas frowned as he looked at it. It was awkward that he had brought no steel-jacketed bullets with him, but he had not expected to find water buffalo on this island. This amazing animal, which, when domesticated, tills the fields of Asia and allows itself to be bullied by small naked boys, is very dangerous in its wild state. The buffalo will charge an intruder out of plain bad temper, and he will follow the charge to the death if fully aroused. Douglas' friend Merian C. Cooper had once seen a tame bull step deliberately in front of a full-grown charging tiger and toss the six-hundred-pound feline so crushingly that Cooper had to put the dying beast out of its pain.

Defosse himself had been tossed and gored by buffalo; Douglas had seen the scars of the horns and had listened to the hunter's clipped account of his miraculous escape. With a small-bore Lebel rifle, one needed to reach the buffalo's brain in order to stop a charge. The buffalo's brain lies at the back of the skull, armored in bone and thick hide which lead bullets will not penetrate. Keep away from them, he thought; that was all they could do today. They would be descending the steep slopes of the bare mountainside soon, and there were no buffalo there or, apparently, in the lowlands either, for they had seen no tracks down there. One of the Malays extended a bamboo stick to Douglas, who promptly took it and chewed on the seared meat.

After a brief meal, the two Malays prepared and inserted into their mouths the red-staining betel nut, Douglas took a final long drink of tea from his canteen, and the party started across the plateau. A cool breeze was blowing, and the declining sun threw a golden light over the scene. Douglas felt revived from the tea, the cooling day and the fresh venison. However, he was wary and alert, for the thought of buffalo was in the back of his mind. He skirted the jungle patches as far as was possible, and stopped frequently to listen. He was forced to pass through one particularly large bamboo thicket, and he kept his nearly useless rifle ready as he did so. The bamboo thicket was like the endlessly repeated vaults of a Gothic church, he thought. The repeated design of arrowy leaves and the stalks leaning together forming the high arch, all green and gold, shadowy but with fragments of the sunshine, the leaves moving and rustling, looking cool and mysterious, and dangerous somehow.

Beyond the bamboo was a clearing, with yet another screen of jungle on the far side. Douglas saw a number of what appeared to be blue pigeons. They were large and fat, and he thought of taking a few of them back to the ship. They fluttered into the second patch of jungle, and Douglas stepped through the barrier of leaves to follow. As he parted the growth, he saw that he was facing another pool of rainwater caught by one of the many lava basins. The water looked fresh and clear. A sudden splashing startled Douglas; with a squawk and the beat of wings, two ducks thrashed up from the pool, circled and arrowed their way low over the jungle. He looked after them in surprise and then laughed at his own start of uneasiness.

Suddenly, behind him, the bamboo thicket crashed and splintered; a man shouted, wood smashed, snorts and a pounding of hoofs struck his ears. He whirled, expecting to see the entire bamboo forest in splinters, for certainly it sounded as if it were being knocked down by a herd of elephants. One of the Malays shouted, "Carabao! Carabao!" Of course, a buffalo! What else would make such a racket? Douglas leaped to his right and out of the screen of growth that encircled the pool. As he emerged into the open he saw an enormous buffalo bull coming at him at full speed. His nose was in the air, his nostrils dilated, and his sweeping horns were laid back almost against his flanks. He was coming like an avalanche! Douglas saw a hundred details in one instantaneous glance; no thought was necessary as to what to do even had there been time for reflection. The animal was only twenty yards away. Quickly he ducked back into the growth and ran his fastest around the basin of water. Thorns tore at him, lianas held him back, leaves were in his eyes. He worked around the pool in jungle so thick he couldn't see five yards in any direction. Then he leaped up on a high rock with jagged sides and stood still, his legs feeling rather weak and trembly as he listened for the buffalo.

Not a sound. The animal had stopped dead still, waiting for a noise to betray an enemy. Douglas held his breath and listened. From somewhere he heard a steady, soft noise, the panting of the buffalo. It was not loud or violent, but it carried a vast menace. He couldn't tell where the sound came from, or how far away the source of it was. The buffalo was certainly standing close-by, waiting. Douglas had remembered that a buffalo does not like to charge into thick jungle. Therefore the animal had stopped at its very edge. There was no sound from the Malays.

It seemed to Douglas that he stood a very long time on the rock. Dusk was beginning to come in the thick jungle, and the bird and animal life was increasing with the cooling of the day. A breeze blew across his face. A cockatoo squawked suddenly in a tree overhead, and Douglas started. Then came a snort, another, the sound of a small tree breaking, and then the diminshing noise of hoofs. The buffalo had given up and was thundering away at a full gallop.

Douglas came down from the rock feeling a little embarrassed. After all, the white hunter, the *Tuan*, was supposed to stand fast before peril and handle dangerous animals as they came along. He smiled a little. Anyone who stood before a buffalo's charge with a useless rifle would not survive very long in the jungle. He waited by the pool until the Malays returned. They grunted when they saw him, and there was no particular expression in the grunts. They retrieved the meat from the bushes where they had dropped it, and the three men moved together through the rolling parkland. When they came out of the last stretch of woods, Douglas was surprised to find the sun still high above the island behind them, though the shadow of the peaks made the descent cool. The shaded outline of the island peaks reached out into the sea, darkening a portion of it; then came sparkling, sun-shot water that glimmered and moved, full of mystery and life. A few white clouds were in the sky. Far below and to the left was Telok Sawa and the *Dog* riding at anchor, a toy ship in an irregularly shaped bathtub.

Still gazing at the marvelous scene before him, the young explorer moved forward. From the corner of his eye he glimpsed a flash of movement in the grass to one side and instinct returned. He stopped, stepped back, and moved to his left until he saw the long thin shape plainly. The hood was beginning to swell. He felt a quick moment of apprehension. A cobra! He had been right to step back. It was well he stopped when he did. High leather boots are good protection, but a big fellow might easily strike too high. The Malays looked at the snake warily, murmured a few words in their own language. Then suddenly the cobra took off at tremendous speed.

Sometimes it is more difficult and tiring to descend a steep mountain than to climb it, and Douglas found this to be true as he led the way toward the ocean. His flapping boot soles tied with strips of rawhide that held them together made each step hazardous. His hands and wrists were bleeding from saw grass cuts, and the sharp lava cut further into his boots. It was a great relief to reach level ground again. He threaded his way carefully through the high grass, eyes alert for the flick of a snake, and emerged at last on the sandy beach with the mountains of Komodo behind him. The sea breeze refreshed him, the soft sand felt good to his feet, and the Malays began to chatter to each other softly.

"What a great day," Douglas said to himself as he moved on up the beach to Telok Sawa.

Defosse and Dunn were there before him. When he had ridden out to the *Dog* in the boat that had come ashore to pick him up, he found Babs and the two men seated in deck chairs under an awning with cold drinks standing at their elbows. Douglas felt hot, sticky, dirty and tired, so he went below at once for a quick change. When he rejoined the group on deck, enthusiasm for all the wonders he had seen that day bubbled forth from him: the parkland, water, woods, rolling plateau, the game, the lizard, the buffalo. Dunn and Defosse were almost equally enthusiastic. They had found many lizard tracks and had seen great quantities of game — deer, boar, and a number of fine game birds, such as jungle fowls, blue pheasants, five or six different kinds of pigeons, turtle doves, quail, and a yellow-legged running hen

Even Defosse, who had until this time yearned only for the Indochinese jungle, was beginning to speak of this island with a gleam in his usually placid eye. As they talked and laughed together, waiting for the evening meal, the sun dropped over the horizon beyond the island, and evening rushed eastward to cover them with coolness. Some of the Malays were drumming softly on the forecastle. Komodo darkened rapidly into utter mystery and stars came out. Douglas looked over the strange island and wondered what was going on there as the shadows of night came down. Were the giant lizards beginning the evening stalk, or were they animals of the daytime only? There, in that jagged shadow, moved and pulsed the world of animals, of birds, snakes, lizards, deer, buffalo — of insects, of death, of life. The world that no man could ever truly be a part of, for he had left it far too many thousands of years ago.

5

The Base Camp

Douglas awoke early the next morning and looked about the small stateroom with something of the sensation with which a boy examines his classroom on the final day of school. The uncertainty of the last few days had vanished; now he knew that the expedition had not been a wild-goose chase. The lizards were there, ashore, waiting for him. With Defosse and Dunn to help, Douglas was sure he could capture several specimens and shoot as many as he had permission to obtain. And today the party would move ashore.

He swung his legs from the bunk and stood up quietly, then went out on deck as the sun came up, gilding the peaks and valleys of Komodo. Defosse joined him there; the two men looked for a few minutes in silence and then went for a quick breakfast. Many things were to be done this day.

After the meal, the boats started ferrying men and

equipment ashore. The sixteen Malays set to work at once building huts at the chosen site, at the head of Telok Sawa, Python Bay. Here the party would be a mere four or five miles from its source of supplies, the SS *Dog*. The ocean breezes blew coolly and steadily, and there seemed to be no mosquitoes. The camp was close to the beach, but set in rich grass and shady trees. Up the shore a hundred yards was a cluster of the strange gubbong palms — trees of immense height, stretching into the sky a quite incredible distance. Birds sang and whistled in the trees around camp; the wind sighed through the palms, and insects hummed a full and changing song.

When Babs joined the group, she was delighted with the place and the arrangements. Six palm leaf huts were ready, their ends open to the sea breeze, with bamboo

Babs Burden and Lee Fai at the base camp.

Burden and Defosse at the Python Bay camp. Defosse is not sticking out his tongue at the photographer; that's a pipe.

platforms for sleeping well above the ground. Chu cooked in one, another was equipped as a dining room, Babe and Douglas occupied a third, Defosse and Dunn another, and the sixteen Malays slept in the other two. Rough chairs and a table were ready in the Burdens' hut. On the table were placed a kerosene lamp, ammunition, notebooks, flashlights, and boxes of medical supplies. The guns were laid across a stout rack, oiled and ready. The place smelled fresh and earthy, and already insects were moving into the thick and rustling palm frond roof. Within days the thatch held spiders, scorpions, centipedes, lizards, and snakes. The cots were on the platform in the rear, well above ground and as far away as possible from insect and reptile life. The cots were covered with mosquito netting; there were no mosquitoes, but every morning the nets were dotted with insect bodies, bits of mud from wasp nests, spiders, and on one occasion a scorpion.

While Babs settled into the camp, the men started hunting. They shot several deer and pigs as bait and with stout ropes tied the carcasses fast to trees. They hoped that the lizards would be attracted by the smell. For a while, they would study and observe only, trying to find out as much as possible about the habits of these weird creatures.

While waiting for the men, Babs wandered along the beach at sunset. Her house was ready; Chu was busy with the evening meal, and now she was half sorry she hadn't gone with Douglas and the others. She had promised herself that she wouldn't be a stay-at-home on this expedition. She was going everywhere the others went, and she had every intention of shooting a dragon lizard herself.

At the beach, she looked around in surprise. Beside every stone a small white flag seemed to be waving. She moved closer to the nearest white flags and they disappeared. She stood and waited quietly, and in a few moments a small crab emerged from beneath every stone. Each started beckoning to the nearest neighbor with one large white claw. They continued this waving until one of the crabs emerged from its own home and sidled over to the opponent's hole. Then began a strange fencing match, claw against claw. The crabs circled, the claws clashed and feinted; the combat was in dead earnest. Finally one of the two duelists would weaken; he would then be pursued and seized by his enemy and dragged down the enemy hole, his white flag still waving. Babs shivered a little. Even the small and ludicrous life on this island appeared deadly, living in constant strife.

The men returned in the dusk, with Lee Fai, the Chinese cameraman, limping along behind with his camera over his shoulder. "Walking much trouble," he said, and groaned expressively.

After supper the Europeans sat around the fire for a time, its heat welcome in the cool night air. Defosse cleaned his rifle, pulled at his mustache, and commented in detail on what he had observed of the island. He was obviously weakening, but every comment ended with an unfavorable comparison between Komodo and the lush jungle country of his Indochinese home.

They went to bed early, and Babs lay on her cot under the rustling roof and watched the moon rise out of the sea. She watched the curling tops of the waves silvered by the moon and went to sleep with the constant roar of the pounding surf in her ears.

Douglas came awake just after dawn, hearing above the background of birdsong a scuttling, thrashing, and muttering outside his hut. Barefooted and pajamaed he ran out only to see Chu ducking gingerly about an object on the ground, waving a large-mouthed bottle in one hand.

"What in the world is it, Chu?" he asked.

Chu made a stab with the bottle, moved it along the ground, and shoved something into it with a stick. Then he clapped on the top and stood up proudly, triumphant over his specimen for Dr. Dunn. Douglas examined the creature with a shudder. It was a black and dark red centipede about twelve inches long. Such creatures were common on the island, along with scorpions the size of a large crawfish.

A minor purpose of the expedition was to collect samples of insect life, as well as the more spectacular reptiles. Douglas realized that collecting the insects would not be difficult. A most interesting exhibit could be secured from the thatched roof of their sleeping hut. Legs of cots and tables were kept in containers of water to discourage insects. Boots were carefully shaken out every morning lest a scorpion be inside. The ants got into the food, even the cold cream and toothpaste.

"Every woman should try being a naturalist's wife just once," Babs grumbled one morning, "just to prove how much she loves her husband. It's great, providing you keep in the spirit of things and learn to love every one of God's creatures; merely laugh shrilly when a centipede emerges from your trousers, when roaches build nests in your shoes, and you can feel the tickling of thousands of feet all over you day and night."

Dr. Dunn, avid herpetologist that he was, went around in a glow of excitement from the richness of the reptile life. On the first morning in the base camp he collected a green pit viper from the roof. Among the poisonous varieties of snakes, Dr. Dunn found within a few days cobras, pit vipers, true vipers, and back-fanged snakes, all abundant. In other words, Komodo, unlike any other part of the world except India, was cursed with all four classes of poisonous snakes. Douglas now realized that all members of the party must be exceedingly careful. He had brought along only a general snake serum, and he was afraid that it would be quite inadequate if someone were bitten by, for example, the Russell's viper.

This dread snake was present on Komodo in numbers, although it was unknown in the rest of eastern Malaysia. Once, when going through the jungle, the Malay behind Douglas started chuckling and grunting in a strange way. He suddenly crouched down and started fumbling at his loincloth. Then with a final explosive grunt he hauled forth a Russell's viper, held firmly by the back of the head. Then he carefully knocked off the fangs with his machete and played with the creature like a child with a toy. After his Central American experiences, Douglas was not new to snake-infested jungle, and he soon recovered the ever watchful eye necessary for survival. For example, he never moved hastily in heavy growth without looking carefully first; he never jumped from rocks or logs into long grass without precaution. He drilled the same routine into Babs so that very soon awareness of the danger became a part of life.

He had been considerably concerned about Babs, and how a city girl brought up with every luxury would take to the relative hardships of camp life in the tropics. But as the routine became established, she seemed to become increasingly fascinated with their doings and in the life itself — except for the insects. She hated ants. They dropped on her from the trees, crawled on her from the ground, stung until she danced with discomfort. But the life seemed to be quite fulfilling to her.

They went to bed as soon as it was fully dark, with the fire flickering through the huts and the surf pounding up a line of white foam. Babs liked the tropical sky at night, velvet black, with new constellations, and the mountains silhouetted against the sky. The Southern Cross rode in splendor against the black. In the morning the cockatoos were their alarm clocks, waking them at first light. They took a dip in the sea and had breakfast. Then they would visit the baits, with guns and cameras, and return for another swim and lunch. After lunch came more hard hunting, until dark.

Late one afternoon Douglas and Babs went out to get some doves or pigeons for supper. They could hear a hundred different calls, but could see nothing except an occasional flash of orange or blue wings. Then, as the sun went down, birds began flying everywhere through the golden light. They both loved this time of day, with the shadows of evening creeping over the land, the air sweetly still, and with marvelous colors reflected from the sky. The growing sounds of evening stole downward from the mountainside as darkness gathered. They turned homeward up the beach, and Douglas shot two ducks practically by moonlight. They could hear the wild pigs grunting around them, and ahead the campfires shone on the circle of huts and the half-naked bodies of Malays. Afterward they had a supper of soup,

A quiet night at base camp finds Chu on kitchen duty, as Dr. Dunn and Babs Burden relax with books.

toast, roast pig, fried potatoes, carrots, rice cakes with syrup, and coffee. Then while Douglas cleaned the guns he and Defosse and Dunn laid plans for the next day. By eight o'clock it was bedtime.

Across the world in New York, people were thinking about getting up. On Komodo, the day was dying, not beginning, and the next morning's sunrise held great promise for excitement. Douglas and his companions went to bed under blankets in the delicious cool of the oncoming night to the sleep-inducing sound of the rhythmic surf.

The main business of the expedition was proceeding well. Daily visits to the baits revealed that small lizards were coming to them in great numbers, and there were signs that one or two larger specimens had paid a visit — a wild pig ripped in half, or a vanished carcass and a broken rope that once had tied it fast. Douglas already had noticed that the dragon lizard's eyesight was extremely keen, so that for the purposes of observation, motion pictures, and collecting, the party must be well shielded from sight. Considerable time was therefore spent in building brush "bomas" at each of the bait sites. These were small huts of brush arranged to look like natural growth, with loopholes from which eyes, guns, or cameras could be directed toward the bait.

Constant restoration of baits was necessary, and Defosse and Douglas hunted every morning and evening. On occasion Babs accompanied them and did her share of the shooting. Wild pig and deer were numerous, so there was little difficulty in obtaining plenty of meat to attract the lizards. So far, most of the specimens observed had been small, but one day Douglas sighted another big one.

It was about 9:30 A.M. at the foot of the pinnacle country that the monster was seen. Douglas was on a gently sloping, cone-shaped hill covered with short grass and a few palm trees. The lizard was working his way

A dragon lizard moving through the grass on Komodo.

downhill, and Douglas sank down into the grass to remain unobserved. The lizard stalked slowly and sedately along, his yellow, forked tongue working incessantly, literally tasting the air for scent of something living or dead. His head was swinging slowly from one side to the other. Against the background of the sun-yellowed grass, he looked black with age, and Douglas could see through his glasses the scars on his hide, souvenirs of many a battle on this forgotten island. Once the lizard stopped and buried his nose deep in the grass, perhaps smelling out a shrew or rat or small lizard as a post-breakfast or pre-lunch tidbit. Three pigs dashed away at a distance, and the armored head was raised and poised, the forked tongue aflicker. Then the dragon seemed to vanish, suddenly he simply wasn't there, and Douglas saw no more of him that day.

The party had been observing the *Varanus komodoensis*, this largest of living lizards, for several days now, and a number of things had been learned. They were plentiful on the island; sometimes the smaller ones came in scores to the baits. Although very sharp of eye, they disregarded sound so completely it was possible to talk aloud without arousing their suspicion. At night, in or-

The two large lizards feeding on one of the baits.

der to avoid the cold, they disappeared into dens dug deep into the earth, an important action for animals with no heating systems such as mammals have. Since they were daylight feeders, it was natural that their sight should be good from dawn to dusk. Their sense of smell, closely related to the incessant working of the long, yellow, forked tongue, was phenomenal. The tongue's constant flickering searched the air currents for odors and carried them directly to the main scent organs themselves.

The big lizards were coming around now. Others of the party saw them here and there; their tracks — bird-like imprints with the mark of the dragging tail visible between them — were seen in several muddy places. Now collecting would start. Douglas wanted to take back a number of dead specimens, in addition to several live lizards. When he urged the importance of attempting to capture some alive, everybody agreed. Douglas himself felt excited at the proposal. Failure or success of the expedition now depended on the events of the next few weeks. He looked across the fire and into the black night from which arose the jagged peaks. The lizards were there. In the morning they would go after them in earnest.

6

The Hunting

The air was cool and the doves were filling the woods with their soft cooing as the party set out the next morning. Douglas led the way with a Malay beside him, then came Babs and Defosse, and then four more Malays. Everyone was refreshed from a cool night's sleep, and in the early morning the going was easy. Douglas came to the edge of a deep and heavily shaded ravine. He looked, then jumped over the edge, dropping about five feet to the ground below. The Malay started to jump, exclaimed something, and drew back, pointing with outstretched hand. Douglas then saw a brownish stone and curl of root resolve itself into a coiled viper. Had the Malay not looked before jumping, he would have landed immediately alongside the reptile, and the expedition might well have suffered a fatality, for the snake was the deadly Russell's viper. Two of the Malays pinned the snake down with long

The "rumah" or lair of
a large dragon lizard.

forked sticks, and a third gingerly picked it up by the
head and knocked off its fangs with his "parang" —
the machetelike knife of the Malay woodsman. Then the
snake was dropped alive into a sack to be carried home
to Dunn.

The ravine led in the general direction of the baited
area, so Douglas took advantage of the relatively easy
walking by following along its sandy floor. Great trees
nearly hid the sky above it, hanging vines looped and
swirled in the air. Doves were beginning to cease their
calling as the day's heat grew. The party covered half a
mile and then they came upon a large cave dug out beneath a tangle of overhanging tree roots. Darkness hid its

contents completely. However, a certain reptilian odor was in the air, for this was the den, or "rumah" of one of the large Komodo lizards. Douglas knew that the great lizards were supreme among the carnivorous animals of Komodo, so the den was not dug for the sake of safety. He believed that the cold-blooded lizards needed the burrow as protection against too great a temperature change. Since the earth retains heat, a hole dug the right distance within it would maintain an even temperature for the twenty-four hours. Without such protection, the lizard would become comatose during the cool nights, while during the extreme heat of noon it might even suffer from excessive heat.

Defosse agreed that the animal was no doubt away from its den hunting, for the lizards were daytime marauders. Douglas moved the tangle of roots and vines aside for a closer look into the burrow and suddenly his entire right forearm caught fire! He leaped back with an exclamation of pain, seeing his hand and arm covered with red ants. He went through an active torment for a few minutes until he and Defosse had brushed the arm and hand clear, and it was some time before the fiery pain subsided. Babs offered her sympathy, and allowed that she preferred scorpions to ants. Douglas could only agree. He knew that these little creatures were among the fiercest that exist on earth; they would even bite into the flame of a match until consumed by it.

Soon afterward, the party left the ravine and moved into the jungle, circling around to approach the boma from the side away from the ravine. From outside, the boma looked like a mass of thick brush and vines. Douglas squeezed through the narrow opening first and checked for earlier entrants, such as snakes. All seemed clear, and the others followed him in. They settled at the loopholes. Lee Fai prepared his movie camera for action.

Bamboos arched to one side, and in the large tree that grew above the bait were many colorful orchids. Birds still called in the distance, and insects hummed. Bird and other animal life was slowing with the heat of the morning, but this was the time of activity for the lizards. The bait was a large dead boar tied to a tree in the sand at the edge of the ravine about thirty feet from the boma. The view up the dry stream was good for about fifty yards.

The group in the boma talked freely. Ants began to arrive in some numbers, not the fire ants of Douglas' previous encounter, but still uncomfortable enough. Small things rustled in the leaves of the boma, and it was easy to imagine all kinds of poisonous, slithering things. Everybody was very watchful as to any movement both outside and inside the structure.

Then Douglas' eyes caught the head of a small lizard

protruding from behind a stone. The wind blew from the bait to the boma, so he knew that the animal couldn't catch the scent of man. After a moment the lizard, a small one three feet long, moved into the open, heading straight for the carcass of the wild pig. It began to eat; then others appeared, varying in size, but all relatively small. Defosse, though still skeptical about the whole undertaking, showed the patience of the trained hunter. He watched and said nothing.

Suddenly all motion in the glade stopped. Each of the half dozen lizards working on the carcass froze into immobility; then, as if at a signal, all turned and dashed away. Everyone in the boma became doubly alert; even Lee Fai was quiet. For long moments nothing moved in the glade. Then Douglas felt Babs start suddenly; then he saw a big black head appear from behind a tree. It remained entirely motionless while the two dark, beady eyes beneath their protruding ridges of bone searched every inch of the surroundings. Douglas saw its eyes turn on the boma and he remained rigid, for the lizards' eyesight was very keen. However the interior of the brush structure was so dark that the humans were invisible from without. The deeply sunken, grim eyes left the boma and turned toward the bait.

"Are you going to shoot him, Douglas?" Babs whispered.

"No — not yet. I think the biggest ones always come last."

The lizard was now assured that all was well, and he lowered his head. The long, yellow forked tongue flashed into view, then in and out so rapidly it made a blur. Douglas knew that the creature was testing the air, and he was doubly glad that the wind remained right. Then the lizard moved toward the bait, great mouth open wide, slime dripping from it as he moved. He looked as if he were about to seize the entire bait in one great gulp. The impression that he gave as he came ponderously forward was one of great weight and strength. Although the smaller lizards looked rather slim and agile, the adults were thickset muscular creatures with very heavy bodies. It was later learned that after a lizard reached the length of seven feet, the weight increased very rapidly; between seven and eight feet the animal roughly doubled in weight. This lizard was about eight feet long, and Douglas was sure that larger ones were in the vicinity.

They watched the great animal feed. Douglas nudged Lee Fai and heard the grinding of the motion picture camera. The lizard paid no attention as he gulped and tore at the pig. He used his long sharp claws to rip and tear with, while the thin, pre-curved teeth with saw-toothed edges were employed to rip off great chunks of the foul meat. The beast maneuvered this by seesawing back and forth on braced legs, giving a wrench at the bait with every backward move. In this position with his jaws buried deep in the meat, and neck curved forward and down, he resembled nothing so much as paintings of *Tyrannosaurus Rex*, restored. When the piece of flesh had been detached, he lifted his head and gulped down the whole slab, even though it was an enormous one. As he swallowed the food, the sides of his neck became distended in a most astonishing fashion. Then the lizard licked his chops, rubbed both sides of his face on the ground as if to clean it, and lifted his head for a careful look at the landscape. The party was to find that if a large lizard was surprised while eating, the results were likely to be most unpleasant, for the animal would immediately disgorge everything he had eaten, to the accompaniment of a dreadful smell.

A big lizard pauses at the bait, a dead and swollen boar.

The camera whirred away, and Douglas was delighted with the footage that was being secured. Now the lizard stood up high in a new fashion, the tail and hind quarters on the ground while the forelegs were braced, his head reaching into the air. He stayed for several minutes in this position; then he sat up on his haunches, with forefeet dangling like those of a rabbit. Again Douglas thought of *Tyrannosaurus Rex*. Something had disturbed the great lizard; his eyes were fixed on the jungle off to one side. Douglas and his companions waited in suspense. Suddenly the lizard turned and dashed away with a speed that belied the former impression of ponderous slowness. Douglas felt very sure that something exciting was about to happen, but for long minutes there was nothing to be seen. He brought his rifle forward to the loophole, drew a cartridge into the chamber, and checked to see that the safety was on.

Then, about fifty yards up the draw, a very large lizard strode magnificently into view. Douglas heard Babs' exclamation and Defosse's pleased grunt. This was a heavy, powerful animal, well over nine feet long, and much the biggest the expedition had seen so far. This was a real dragon, Douglas thought. He would do perfectly for the habitat group of Komodo Dragon Lizards at the American Museum of Natural History. He asked Lee Fai to start photographing the animal at once, and watched with delight as the lizard advanced cautiously step by step, the great bulk of his body held clear of the ground. He was a rugged creature, black as dead lava, whose every aspect spoke of a great stretch of time. Douglas wondered how many scores of years had weathered that bony armor. As the lizard drew closer and raised himself on muscular forelegs, Douglas could see the blistered scars and indentations of his thick hide. Once at the bait, the lizard stood up on his hind legs and scanned the entire area, the long yellow tongue flickering. Then he began his feast, but this specimen didn't seem content with ripping chunks from the tied-down boar. Instead, he took the whole pig in his jaws and started rocking back and forth with all his power, trying to wrench it free. The seesaw motion was so violently performed that Douglas was afraid a rope might break at any moment, and he could not bear the thought of losing this animal. He let Lee Fai grind out a few more feet of film, then sighted down the barrel of his Lebel rifle.

There was no question of marksmanship, with the target relatively still at a distance of only thirty feet. But he could take no chance of the animal escaping, so he quickly squeezed the trigger. The lizard fell backward; its tail thrashed back and forth like a flail, raising a cloud of sand and dust. Then the mortally wounded creature raised his head once more before collapsing to the ground. The tail twitched again and all was still. Douglas let out a long breath.

The big lizard made a notable load on the return trip to camp. It was estimated to weigh well over two hun-

Above is the habitat group in the Hall of Reptiles of the American Museum of Natural History in New York. These are the lizards collected by Douglas Burden. Below is a closer view of the lizard at the left in the group.

dred and fifty pounds. This lizard, with two more, is on view today in the Hall of Reptiles, American Museum of Natural History, in New York City. The habitat group reproduces faithfully the growth, background, landscape and feeling of Komodo. Douglas knew that this would be the fate of the animal he had killed, and the thought that he had given it a sort of immortality removed any bad feeling about having bushwacked the beast from a baited blind.

In the glade beside the ravine, the small lizards, it may be assumed, soon returned and tore hungrily at the remains of the boar until nothing was left. So the next morning the party went to another jungle clearing that had been well baited with deer and pig. No shooting was planned for this day unless an unusual specimen came along. Instead, Defosse was going to try his luck at trapping alive some of the moderately sized lizards. Eight Malays bearing heavy bamboo poles and many lengths of rope accompanied the group. Lee Fai was

A close-up view of the two lizards at the right in the habitat group shown on the facing page.

Members of the expedition building a trap on Komodo.

taking sick leave that day, and Douglas was going to act as cameraman.

Trap and bait were ready. The trap consisted of a circle of heavy stakes, with a vee of stakes leading into it. The stakes, side and top, were covered with brush and limbs until the whole looked like a mass of bushes. In the circular area was the bait, a rotted deer carcass to please the lizards' taste for well-hung meat. Near the front of the trap stood a stout sapling with a rope dangling from its top. Defosse, in fluent Malay and by example, showed the men what he wanted them to do. Together they hauled on the rope until the sapling was bent over, just above the neck of the trap. A noose was tied at the lower end, Defosse arranging it around the entrance like a giant snare, with a clever wooden trigger that would be tripped when a lizard tried to enter the trap for the enticing deer meat. When the trap was set, the party settled into the boma to wait, with the Malays hidden with them or waiting back in the nearby jungle.

This time the wait was not a long one. Several small lizards gathered; when they approached the bait Defosse frightened them away with stones. Then a six-foot specimen appeared, and instantly all the smaller lizards

Bending over the spring pole for another dragon trap.

scampered away. Defosse was muttering to himself in French, expressing various endearments and enticements to make the lizard approach the bait. It did so, slowly, and with many pauses to search the area with its darting eyes. The tongue was a flickering yellow blur. Closer, closer. Now the snout, with toothed jaws already opening in anticipation, was being shoved through the entrance.

There came a snap, a broken hiss, a twang, and the lizard was jerked high in the air, twisting and fighting savagely. Defosse burst from the brush shelter, a lasso in his hand, with the Malays beside him. The lizard was dangling head high, and the ropes flew. Within minutes the creature was tied fast with several lines. One of the heavy bamboo poles was thrust through the loops and the lizard was carried off in triumph back to camp while Defosse set the trap a second time.

Five more medium-sized lizards were caught that day, and the Malays were hot and weary before all of them had been carried back to camp, where they were placed in cages brought along for the purpose. Douglas complimented Defosse warmly on the success of his trap; the tough Frenchman smiled with pleasure and assured him that they could have as many lizards alive as they wanted.

Since this was obviously so, Douglas decided not to

keep any of the lizards except the largest one, which was about seven feet long. The expedition still had some weeks to remain in Komodo, and he thought it useless to feed and handle the lizards during that time. Accordingly, five lizards were released near the beach in an effort to determine whether they would take to the sea of their own free will — an important question with regard to their highly restricted distribution. Of the five lizards let loose, one large and one small one fled to the sea without hesitation. Two headed for the jungle, while the fifth ran down the beach for a hundred and fifty yards, went into the grass, then deliberately turned and walked down to the water's edge. He swam far out into the bay. The largest one, which had taken to the water immediately, remained submerged for a full two minutes, then reappeared a hundred yards away. It swam down the beach for half a mile, walked ashore, and ambled slowly off into the jungle. When swimming at the surface with head well above water, and long, undulating tail, the Komodo dragon gave every appearance of a sea serpent. Yet on the whole, the lizards did not appear to be first-class swimmers, their movements being somewhat clumsy and ineffective.

Thus one more fact was added to the growing store of knowledge that the expedition was gathering about the dragon lizards of Komodo.

7

The Move

Information about Komodo Island life was growing steadily; Dr. Dunn already had made a significant collection of reptiles, and the lizard specimens were rapidly accumulating. But Douglas began to feel that perhaps they had exhausted the possibilities of this vicinity, at least for new sights and new species. He had not forgotten the beautiful parkland he had found on the plateau on the first day's exploring, and now his thoughts returned to it with force. The plateau, above which further peaks rose into the sky, would provide quite another environment for the animal life of the island, for it would be much cooler than the jungle and beach area, and perhaps be blessed with more moisture. He consulted with Dunn and Defosse and it was decided to move the base camp into the mountains.

Immediately Douglas took Defosse and half of the Malays up to the site he remembered so well. The climb was worse than he had thought it to be, and even the tough Defosse was ready for rest when they reached the top. He was enthusiastic about the prospects and the country, however, and Douglas left him there with the natives to prepare a camp, and then once more faced the climb down the lava slopes.

Only a minimum of equipment would be carried to the new camp and the next day was occupied with sorting out what would be taken. One of the first jobs was to transfer two live lizards into a new and stronger cage. He missed the experienced Defosse in this job, for the animals were stubborn to the last degree. He and the Malays set the cages end to end and opened the doors between them. The lizards huddled at the far end of their cage, hissing like angry steam engines. Douglas prodded them with a bamboo stick and the hissing redoubled; the animals clawed at the mesh and each other, but clung fast to the end of the cage. Finally Douglas tied dried grass to the end of a stick, set fire to it, and inserted it into the cage. This had the desired effect, and one after the other, their red mouths open, their jaws dripping slime, they rattled into their new home, hissing horribly, lashing their tails and scratching so violently at the steel mesh that their claws came off. Two Malays had to be left at the base camp to look after things, under the daily supervision of the captain of the SS *Dog*.

On that afternoon, Babs had a fishing adventure. She had already had some success fishing for the many species that lived in the reefs and rocks surrounding the island. Now she wanted new worlds to conquer. With Dunn's assistance, she rigged a line of quarter-inch manila, tied an immense hook on the end, and baited it with a chunk of deer meat. She announced that she was going to catch one of the huge fish they had seen cruising off the beaches. The grinning skipper of the *Dog* had his boat's crew row the hook and bait through the the line of surf and drop it into deep water beyond a ledge.

It was a long wait, but finally the line which had been rather slack in the surf began moving, then tightening. Babs ran back up the beach until all slack was gone, set her heels and gave a tremendous yank, thereby setting the hook. Then she was pulled forward several feet, and the line started moving to the right. She hung on, dragged closer and closer to the water's edge. Dunn came to her assistance, but she warned him back. This shark, or whatever, was hers alone.

The battle went on for ten minutes at least. Babs was wet, and the sand was plowed with the evidence of struggle. But the creature at the end of the line was tiring, and foot by foot the determined young woman brought it in. At last the dark shape showed intermittently in the line of tumbling surf, was dragged through, and, hauled by the line and carried by a wave, stranded on the beach.

Her quarry was an enormous grouper, or sea bass, thick and solid, and certainly much heavier than she was. The natives swarmed down in delight, while Babs demanded that Douglas get out the camera and make a record of the big one that didn't get away. After which, while the Malays cleaned and cut up the fish in anticipation of a feast, she wiped the sweat from her face and returned to her hut for a well-earned rest in the shade.

The next day was a tough one for Babs. Even though the party started at dawn to make the most of the cool of the day, by the time they had made their way up to the first ridge of the foothills, climbing up and down gullies, weaving through rocks, cutting through dense undergrowth, and struggling through hip-high saw

Babs Burden and her grouper.

grass, the morning had grown intensely hot, without a trace of a breeze. Progress had been slowed by the loads everyone was carrying, and by Lee Fai lagging mournfully in the rear. It had been further slowed by the necessity of using extreme care to avoid snakes, which had turned out to be far more numerous on Komodo than anyone had expected. Once a deadly cobra slithered through the grass between Dunn and Babs, disappearing instantly in the yellow sea of growth. One of the Malays was stung in the foot by a small scorpion, which added to the care with which the others put their hands out of sight in leaves or grass.

On a higher ridge they stopped and rested in the shade of a giant gubbong palm. The view below was lovely, but the blackened slopes of lava still ran above them. Babs was definitely unhappy. Lee Fai looked up the slope and groaned pitifully. Douglas, knowing that a tough climb still lay ahead, lied cheerfully and told them that it wasn't as bad as it looked.

It wasn't. It was twice as bad.

A fall on the jagged lava was dangerous and the saw grass ripped and stung. The sun glared down, beat off the lava, and roasted them. It was like a furnace. They stopped often to rest, wet with sweat, itching from insects and saw grass, heads throbbing, eyes half shut from the glare, hands and legs bleeding. On they went, on and up. Even the wiry Malays were very quiet, moving with silent determination beneath their loads. Lee Fai was left farther and farther in the rear. Slowly, ever so slowly, they approached their goal. They were all thoroughly done in. Now the last rise of ground was a hundred yards away, now fifty. Douglas encouraged Babs by pointing it out, and she climbed with new vigor. At last they reached the top. Without pausing, Douglas led the way onto the lip of ground that overlooked their camping site. He heard with pleasure Babs' gasp of surprise and delight.

Below them was the rolling, parklike country, dotted here and there with patches of jungle and palm trees. Close ahead the sunlight glinted off a large pool of water. Trees overhung one side, making it shady and cool. Beyond the pool was a circle of palm huts, open at both ends to the breeze. A few Malays moved among the huts; a deer hung in the shade of one of the flowering mimosa trees surrounding the camp. The wind rippled across the mellow fields of grass — like waves of changing color. A few fluffy clouds floated against a hard azure sky.

"It's heaven!" Babs said in disbelief.

Defosse and his crew came to greet them and took the loads from the exhausted carriers. They strode downhill through the rustling grass, and at the edge of the huts

Chu, who had come up the day before, met them with his wide grin and a wooden tray of glasses of tea, cooled from immersion in the pool of water. Rough seats were waiting in the shade of the pool, and the exhausted travelers sank into them and took full advantage of Chu's offering. Babs gave a great sigh of relief, took off her hat, and leaned back with her eyes closed, the cool breeze ruffling her hair. Very soon, when they began to feel rested again, Lee Fai came staggering down the last hill like a man who had crossed the great American desert. He babbled over and over again, "Walking much trouble, walking much trouble!" And then he burst out laughing. Douglas suspected that it was half hysteria, for even now Lee Fai's notions were such that he half expected to find a tiger lurking behind every tree.

In the late afternoon, Chu served a delicious meal, in his usual surprising fashion. It began with a strong, nourishing soup, the origin of which, Douglas suspected, was deer horns in velvet — one of Chu's favorites. The main dish was ever more delectable, and much more potent and mysterious. Even Defosse could not name the ingredients. After everyone had guessed wildly, Douglas complimented Chu enthusiastically and asked him for an explanation. Chu grinned joyously from ear to ear and said nothing. They never did discover what was in the dish.

When supper was finished, Babs announced her intention of having a bath in one of the other nearby rocky pools. When Douglas invited her on a scouting trip, she declined with thanks, saying that she had had torture enough for one day. Defosse was, as always, eager to be on the move, so he and Douglas took their rifles and strode off into the cooling late afternoon.

Fresh buffalo tracks were everywhere, so they were very wary of every thick clump of bamboo. If one passed too close, a buffalo was likely to surprise one with a charge that left little opportunity to escape. On their way up to the divide they saw many deer and wild boar, and pigeons of every variety. The booming, soft, sad voices of doves resounded from every clump of jungle. Douglas thought that this was ideal country to hunt over, the uneven terrain making stalking an easy matter. As they reached the backbone of the ridge, a big buck sprang up before them and coughed, a strangely miserable sound for so beautiful a creature. From the crest they could look down all around to a sunlit sea dotted here and there with islands of indescribable shapes that stood out like dark shadows against the silver of wind-swept water. The sun was setting and the western sea glowed blood-red with the embers of dying day. To Douglas, standing there on the mountaintop, the island beneath his feet seemed like a great ship sailing a painted sea.

Then they came to a water hole, and in the mud

around it they saw Varanus tracks, bird feet with the mark of the dragging tail between them. In the hillside nearby was a great hole, the rumah, under a massive boulder. Before the boulder was a level spot. Here, obviously, the beast disported himself and basked in the sunshine, warming bone and muscle after the chill night to make himself limber and quick before embarking on the hunts of the day.

Soon afterward, while the mist crept up the thickly wooded gulches and the moon swam above the palm trees, Douglas and the old hunter fell to talking, as they had so many times before in other wild places.

"One might take many walks in many countries of the world," Defosse said softly, "and not have one half as interesting as this has been. I would like to bring my whole family and settle here, and be King of Komodo."

Thus the jungle hunter articulated his surrender to the wild, weird beauty of Komodo, and admitted that this island and its mysteries might even be superior to French Indochina, which heretofore had held all his loyalties.

When the two men returned to camp, everyone had gone to sleep except two Malays who were playing their bamboo flutes by a campfire that had dropped to red coals, brightened occasionally by a passing breeze. There was the glisten of a white moon on dew-wet grass, and the murmur of small voices out of the leafy darkness of the nearby jungle. Douglas could hear the gentle rustle of a sleepy forest talking to itself. Never, he thought, had there been a more enchanting night. He heard the wind rattle in green bamboo, smelled the fragrance of flower-scented glades, and he thought with pleasure of how little importance man held here. The spirit of the place was sighing on the night wind, with every breath of air that stroked these ancient hills. Now there was a ghostly murmur reminiscent of aeolian music in a pine forest. What magic the moon makes, Douglas thought, and how inexpressibly subtle is the charm of such a scene.

8

The Plateau

I n the high altitude of the plateau, the nights became truly cold during the late hours. Douglas was sleeping under two wool blankets, and they were not too much. The morning reminded him of early morning in the Canadian wilderness. The sun was just rising, bathing the pool, the huts, and the golden fields of grass with their clumps of trees in a warm, ruddy light. The air was crisp and fresh with a slight breeze. Except for the absence of the scent of pine needles and the sound of the white-throated sparrow's lovely wilderness chant, he could easily have imagined himself thousands of miles away in North America. He rolled from the cot and walked to the open end of the hut. Babs heard him stirring, and opened a sleepy eye. Douglas could smell coffee boiling, and Babs sat up and sniffed. Then she joined him at the door, and they smiled with the delight of being in a strange and wonderful place, with days of adventure stretching before them.

After Chu's substantial breakfast had been eaten, plans for the day were made. They decided to kill deer and pigs for bait and build blinds near the carcasses, in hopes of attracting, photographing, and capturing larger specimens than those they had already observed and secured. Defosse and Babs would go north, Douglas south. As for Dunn, he pointed beyond the rolling land that encircled their camp to a great black wood that swept up the steep mountain slopes and merged with the cloud forest above. He wanted to visit that wood in search of specimens. And so the day was planned.

Accompanied by two Malays, Douglas set out while the air was still cool and invigorating. Before he had covered a mile he encountered a group of wild pigs, not too far from the rumah of a lizard. He had a close shot at the big boar leading the group, and the animal dropped at the report. Douglas frowned. Too easy, but it was in a good cause.

First the boar was tied to a strong root, and then the three men set to work to build a blind about thirty feet away. All three had become accustomed to this task, and half an hour saw it completed. Then the small party continued on, searching for a new location and a new bait. They had traveled for about two hours when on topping a rise of ground they saw an enormous solitary buffalo bull. He had a magnificent sweep of horns. The bull was lying down near the edge of a bamboo thicket. He was a formidable-looking animal. This was game that was dangerous — mighty different from shooting a deer or even a wild boar. Douglas reached into a pocket of his jacket and brought out a handful of steel-jacketed cartridges. Quickly and quietly he reloaded his rifle. The two Malays faded behind him into tall grass and in the direction of another clump of woods.

Douglas considered the situation. He was about 200 yards away but such was the lie of the land and the direction of the wind that it was quite impossible to get closer without running the risk of being seen or smelled. These Komodo buffalo, unlike their relations in Indochina, often entered the cover of jungle, coming out to feed principally at night. Nevertheless, when attacked they preferred to stand their ground in the open and rarely retreated into thick growth.

Douglas knelt down and aimed very carefully, trying for a vital point just behind the shoulder, since the animal was lying broadside-on. The sights were steady; they were adjusted for the range, and the shot would be dead center. Douglas squeezed the trigger and the rifle cracked out in the hot silence. Immediately the bull lurched to his feet and strode defiantly right out into the open sunlight and stood there with legs far apart and head thrown back, a spectacle of dauntless courage. Because of the angle at which the sun hit his body, the gigantic muscles of his neck and shoulders stood out in beautiful relief, so that he gave the impression of tremendous power. He made a fine target, and Douglas fired again. There was a spurt of dust in front of the buffalo. He could not believe it. When he fired again, he began to sense that something was wrong. The shot sounded flat and the kick was not what it should have been. He fired again and again, and each time the bullet fell short.

The answer was simple, though it could have been a fatal one. Although Douglas didn't realize it, the barrel of his rifle was an old secondhand French war one. It had begun to wear out, and as the bullets no longer fitted tightly in the grooves, they were dropping two or three feet in each hundred yards.

Now the bull tossed his head in the air, shook his great horns, pounded his heavy forehoofs on the ground and whirled this way and that with sudden vicious movements, as if searching for the source of danger. Douglas thought that any hunter would be proud to bag such a magnificent beast.

He realized quite well from the bull's manner that he was looking for trouble, and that if he located the source of the firing he might well charge. Douglas did not like it for this was one of the most dangerous game animals in the world.

When the magazine was empty, the bull must have decided that he had been peppered long enough for, although Douglas was certain that he had not been seen, the buffalo started in his direction at a full gallop but not directly toward him. For a few seconds Douglas stayed where he was, watching the great, thundering beast approach, a cloud of dust rising in his wake. Then jumping up, he ran. Getting a little knoll of ground between himself and the bull he turned and looked once more. The bull was still coming at top speed, head up, and apparently quite unharmed. Douglas made up his mind to join the Malays, who already were in headlong flight. He even determined to pass them; once you decide on a policy of flight there can be no object in loitering. There is nothing but good sense in running away when you know that nothing is to be gained by holding your ground. He was gaining on the others when the three of them dove to safety into the jungle. The bull failed to follow. The Malays were thoroughly disgusted, but even so Douglas managed a rather nervous laugh at his ignominious retreat. Twice now Douglas had failed in his encounters with the buffalo of Komodo. He and Defosse experimented with the Lebel. Firing at a target, they discovered that the bullets were dropping as much as four inches in thirty yards. The rifle barrel was indeed worn out. In the early evening, Douglas and the Frenchman went out after a buffalo for meat. This time they found a young bull grazing in the open, less than a hundred yards away. Thanks to Defosse's expert marksmanship and fine rifle, they promptly secured him.

Babs had stayed in camp this time, for her nerves were somewhat on edge. She and Defosse had been working on a blind in the afternoon and buffalo had come close. By some oversight, Defosse had failed to bring along steel bullets, so the two of them had been forced to crawl up on a big rock, much as Douglas had during his first encounter with a buffalo on this island.

"I can't describe how relieved I was to be on the rock," Babs told her husband. "There was a whole herd of wild buffalo. In the future I won't be seen much on terra firma; I will only be happy when perched on rocks or in trees. And I don't even like that too well for I keep imagining cobras slithering by!"

As for Dunn, he came back vastly pleased with his trip into the black wood. Upon entering it, he saw in the first few yards a rare black cobra, a centipede of enormous proportions, scorpions, bats, and some other horrible creatures that were to him enormously attractive. He had prowled around in the wood for hours, lost himself, had a wonderful time, and finally emerged with a smile of glee and a varied assortment of venomous creatures which were exhibited to everybody proudly and then immersed in formaline. Defosse called this area of jungle the Prehistoric Wood and refused to go into the place. Douglas and Babs decided immediately that they would have to explore it the first thing the following morning.

They did so, and as soon as they moved into its dank, chilly darkness, the bright morning sun was at once totally hidden. They had a feeling of being entangled in something very unpleasant. They kept going, however, clutching their rifles and watching every step. It was gloomy and dark. Douglas moved by compass, not wanting to spend too much time in there, though always they could have found their way out simply by traveling downhill. After an hour they penetrated to the very heart of the forest — a place where great blocks of porous lava were strewn prodigiously in every direction, and deep bat-haunted caves filled the couple with wonder. Everywhere there were coiling vines and contorted creepers that dangled through midair from the green canopy above. Giant hawsers, twisted, gnarled and knotted, ugly in shape, hung suspended overhead. Giant lianas encircled the most beautiful trees in a vise-like embrace, causing strangulation. Air-breathing plants sprouted from every limb, plants that never touched root to ground but took their food from the air itself. In all the aisles of the jungle grew superb specimens of the banyan tree, from the sweeping branches of which cables plunged to the ground. These cables take root, feed and support the branch so that it in turn can drop new stems to earth and raise new branches in the air. On all sides were inextricable tangles of knotted, musty and undulating roots that crawled over the earth until they united and rose in the form of a flying buttress, thus to support some monarch of the jungle.

Douglas and Babs plunged through this place of gloom where death seemed to lurk in every byway and at last, following a buffalo trail, they emerged in one step from dismal solitudes into the light of day. It was a vast relief to get out of that musty, stifling forest and stand in the open sunlight once more with the wind in their faces and the waving grass about their feet, the bay below them and a view of mountains rising one above the other into the hazy distance.

They had been standing there only a few minutes enjoying the breeze and the wonderful view when suddenly a big, black dragon lizard emerged from the Prehistoric Wood, to their left. At the same moment a wild boar trotted out in his direction from an isolated clump of bamboo in front of Douglas and Babs. Now at last, Douglas thought, they might see something interesting which would prove definitely whether or not a *Varanus komodoensis* dared to attack a full-grown boar. He motioned Babs down, and they sank into the grass, while Douglas took out his field glasses in order to watch more closely.

The lizard was motionless at the edge of the jungle, watching the boar who trotted unsuspectingly toward him. The lizard, fearing perhaps that he might be seen by the boar, then slid silently into the forest. At this moment, the boar caught the lizard's scent and headed off toward a small patch of jungle at right angles to his former course. Presently the lizard reappeared and, seeing no boar, wandered leisurely out across the open, stopping at frequent intervals to have a good look. About this time the pig emerged from his patch of jungle, saw the lizard headed away in the opposite direction and, satisfied that his route was now clear, ambled along in his original course, stopping now and then to root. The lizard apparently saw the boar out of the back of his head, for he suddenly turned, ducked, and headed back after the pig. The boar saw him coming and ran away into the Prehistoric Wood. So the affair ended, and Douglas realized that he could not reach a verdict on that evidence. However, he didn't believe for a moment that enough animals died a natural death on Komodo to supply thousands of the dragon lizards with food. Therefore, since small mammals were not in sufficient abundance on the island, Douglas felt reasonably certain that the large lizards killed deer and pig for a living.

Babs Burden and her "pet," a medium-sized lizard.

The golden days went by, with something exciting or delightful on every one. Babs hunted as ardently as anyone. Then came a memorable day for her. The party had breakfasted as usual at the first streak of dawn, but Defosse and Babs did not get away until the sun was already gilding the tops of the great gubbong palms. The dew was still heavy underfoot, and the myriad liquid sounds of the jungle were once more coming to life. Babs thought that she would never become accustomed to the rosy wonder of a Malayan dawn, so sudden that the world was bathed in moonlight at one moment and in sunlight the next. Just as sudden was the change in the temperature. Shivering over breakfast, they were wrapped up in all their blankets. With the coming of the sun they shed blankets like a moth sheds its cocoon. They always started the day's hunting in the thinnest of clothes, never forgetting their helmets, which were absolutely necessary against the heat of the tropical sun. As they neared the tree to which they had tied the dead deer the day before, Defosse said to Babs, "You must always be careful when passing these bamboo thickets, for the buffalo are liable to be resting in the shade during the day, and may charge out upon you." He had hardly finished speaking when, with a terrific crashing and a bellow, a great dark gray bull galloped from the side opposite them and disappeared in the nearby jungle.

"Thank God for that," Defosse said, and they continued on their way, Babs with legs that felt strangely like jelly. Douglas had told her that Defosse once had been gored and nearly killed by a water buffalo. They were numerous on Komodo, but not as plentiful as the deer and wild boar, which were everywhere.

When they reached the blind they saw that the bait had been torn completely in half, and the entire hindquarters devoured. It had to be a dragon lizard, and from the looks of the remains, Defosse said that it had been done in one great gulp. No lizard was then in sight, but the old hunter found tracks leading away. He followed them down the hill on one side, while Babs looked around the other. Suddenly something caught her attention on the edge of the jungle to her right. She saw the black head of a giant lizard pointed straight at her. It could have been the same animal that had torn the deer in two. For a moment, the lizard stood partly concealed by the leafy jungle, and then with heaving flanks and ponderous movements he crawled forth into the full light. Babs sank motionless into the tall grass, not realizing that she had put herself between the lizard and the bait.

As he approached step by step, the great bulk of his body held clear of the ground, his head, with eyes deep in their sockets, swinging from side to side, she thought of the incredible beasts that had lived in the world millions of years before. He hardly seemed to belong to her world; more fitting, she thought, that he should have crawled up from some bottomless gulch in the earth. This was a hoary customer whose every aspect spoke of great age. He was as black as dead lava.

When he stopped and raised himself on his forelegs to look around, she could see the blistered battle scars and indentations on his bony armor. Then, as he drew nearer, she suddenly realized her predicament. Her rifle was propped against the blind, where she had left it a few minutes earlier! Defosse was out of sight, and the great reptile was continuing straight toward her. Terror flooded through her. Should she jump up and run? What would he do if she did? He might dash away into the jungle, and they would lose the largest lizard the party had seen for some time. Should she lie without moving on the chance that Defosse would come back and shoot him, or that he would change his course and pass her by?

Nearer he came, and nearer, this fearsome creature, with grim head ponderously swinging from side to side. Terror grew, pinning Babs motionless in the grass. She heard the soft hissing that sounded like a gust of evil wind, and watched the action of that darting, snakelike tongue. The lizard was only yards away. Too late now to leap from hiding! That would be too risky at this short range. She had seen the amazing quickness with which the great lizards could move in an emergency. It was a frightening moment!

Just then she saw Defosse's head appearing over the hill. He whipped his rifle to his shoulder and fired, and she felt the impact of the muzzle blast. The lizard thrashed over on his back, tail whipping dust from the ground. Then he was on his feet and crashing toward the jungle. Defosse fired again and the lizard thrashed, hissed, and died.

Babs was mighty happy to get back to camp that evening and tell Douglas of her big adventure.

9

Capturing a Giant

The days moved rapidly past, each with something new to offer. Babs began to understand the charm of the naturalist's and explorer's life, snakes or no snakes, bugs or no bugs. Even ants she could accept for the privilege of living through this time of action and enchantment. Cold nights, cool dawns, hot golden mornings, sweltering afternoons when the sea breeze felt delightful, and then the quick dusk and the warmth of a fire and wool flannels — it was increasingly delightful.

Babs and François Defosse had by this time become good friends, and she often accompanied the old hunter into the jungles and onto the open fields of grass. He seemed to enjoy having her along, and Douglas was always comfortable when his wife was out with Defosse, in whose prowess and coolness he had the utmost faith. So it was that one fine morning Babs went with Defosse to a baited blind in the woods. Skeletons and hides of half a dozen more *Varani* were wanted to fill the quota allowed by the Dutch governor, and since those on the plateau seemed to be larger than the ones on the coastal plain, it had been decided to shoot a number of them now. Therefore Defosse scouted carefully ahead to the blind, then returned for Babs in the woods, saying that nothing but a few small ones were at the bait. After this they went to the boma and settled themselves into its dark interior, rifles ready. Babs had decided that today was the day she would get one; for too long, she thought, she had been following in the footsteps of the men and never getting a shot at anything. It was always, "Lie down, here comes a deer," or "Stay here, and don't move in case some animal comes in sight." From now on, she was going to shoot, willy-nilly, at least until she had the satisfaction of bagging a fine specimen. Lie down, indeed! She moved her rifle a little closer, and kept her eyes on the clearing and the odorous mass of the bait.

She saw him come from the woods. Not one of the largest, but well worth taking. She glanced over at Defosse, hoping that he hadn't seen, and she caught his smile and wink. She warmed again to François. She was sure he knew exactly how she felt and would wait for her to shoot. Very well; she would wait until the lizard was feeding.

As usual the lizard inspected the clearing and the boma first, and Babs held her breath, though she was certain that the inside was too dark to allow him to see her. Curious over something, the lizard sat up on his hind legs, front feet drooping in against his chest, and covered the clearing again with his eyes, the yellow tongue in constant activity, tasting the air. Defosse didn't move. Babs tried to still her trembling hands, and quietly unclicked the safety on her rifle.

The lizard dropped to all four feet and came rapidly toward the bait. Two smaller ones streaked for the woods, having stayed to the last moment for a final mouthful. The large lizard arrived at the bait, looked around once more, and settled to his feeding.

Babs was shaking, the leaves in the blind were trembling with her rifle barrel's contact. She pushed the muzzle through the loophole, told her hands to stop shaking, lined the sights on the animal's neck, and fired. He jerked convulsively, whirled, and ran for the woods. Babs worked the bolt, and fired again just as the lizard reached the top of the hill and was about to disappear into the woods. At the shot he rolled back down the hill, coming to rest in a clump of brush. In that instant, a second lizard as large as the first burst from another clump and ran for the jungle. Defosse fired once, and the second lizard fell

Babs' hands were shaking again now as Defosse smiled at her and the two of them went to inspect their trophies. Her lizard was ugly even in death, black eyes still open, slimy yellow tongue draped sideways from his

mouth, jaws apart. For no more than a fraction of a
second she felt half sorry she had killed the animal, then
she sensed a glow of pleasure and accomplishment. After
all, they were not exactly lovable animals, at best.

Babs decided that she didn't want to wait alone in the
jungle, and went with Defosse to get help to carry home
the dead lizards. They were back at the blind in an hour,
and Babs was astonished to find her lizard gone. There
had been no doubt that he was dead, so something had
carried him off. Defosse pointed to the tracks leading
off into the jungle, and the marks of a heavy body being
dragged. Another lizard, apparently even larger, had
taken Babs' specimen.

Looking almost excited, Defosse led the way along
the tracks until suddenly they heard a great hissing in
the jungle ahead. The pair topped a rise, and saw another lizard dragging the body of the first one, having
all too evidently eaten all of his insides. Babs looked in
horror at the mess, and then Defosse fired and killed the
third animal instantly. Here was proof indeed that the
dragon lizards were cannibals. No wonder the smaller
ones fled to the jungle at first indication that one of their
larger relatives was approaching.

On the way home, Babs and Defosse went ahead of
the heavily loaded Malays, and just as they passed a
bamboo thicket a buffalo bellowed and crashed out of it.
Defosse screamed "Drop!" and Babs dropped flat. She

didn't see the buffalo charge, but she felt the ground shake under his footsteps, and for a brief second she almost expected to feel the horns and hoofs of the creature. Then he was gone, and when Babs rose to her feet her knees were like water. She had reached camp before she remembered her previous determination not to lie down again when an animal appeared.

She found Douglas in a state of considerable excitement. For some time they had been sure that a lizard larger than any they had yet encountered occasionally emerged from the deep labyrinths of the Prehistoric Wood. Whole deer had been jerked from lashings and carried away, with the lizard tracks large and deeply sunken into a soft section of earth. A lizard had gotten into one of Defosse's larger traps, taken the bait, ripped down the spring pole, and smashed the trap. He had gotten his head free of the noose and had carried away with him the pig carcass with which the trap was baited. Now the Malays reported having seen an especially ugly monster on the edge of the black woods, and they had described it as the largest "land crocodile" yet seen.

Defosse decided that this was a particularly old and wary animal, since it had been seen only once during their time on the plateau. In view of this wariness, plus the animal's size and strength, the expert thought it would be best to build an extra large trap near the edge of the forest, bait it very plentifully, and wait close by in a boma, ready to run out and lash him to a pole as soon as he was caught in the noose. Douglas agreed, and on the following day the necessary preparations were made.

A large boar was shot for bait and placed at the chosen spot to ripen. Heavy stakes were then pounded in the ground all around the bait, except for the usual large opening at one end. The stakes were lashed together very strongly and the whole contraption camouflaged with extreme care. A live tree of considerable size stood by the trap entrance — Defosse wouldn't trust to a cut sapling for the job. The branches were trimmed, a rope tied to the top, and then, with the combined strength of all eighteen men, the tree was bent over and the noose set at the opening in the trap. There was to be one difference between this set and all the others they had built. Douglas didn't want a small lizard to ruin their chances for the big one. It could easily spoil the whole effort if this happened, for the wary old animal they were after would no doubt be lurking in the vicinity to assure himself that all was well. Therefore the release, instead of being automatic, was triggered by a cord that ran along the ground to the boma. The trap would not go off until the cord was pulled. In this way, Douglas could watch everything that went on and release the spring pole just at the right second to send the dragon whirling aloft. The party could then rush out and lash him fast. The cord leading to the boma was well concealed, and the boma itself made almost unnoticeable. Douglas tested the trap several times, and each time the cord was pulled the tree swished upward in a most gratifying manner. Already he could visualize the great lizard dangling in midair, struggling at the end of the rope and ready for capture. The whole device was Defosse's design and handiwork and Douglas found it as pleasing to the eye as to the imagination.

The next morning the dragon hunters were on the job early, for the bait had already begun to smell and attract lizards. For a long time the party waited in the boma — Douglas, Babs, Defosse, and several Malays. They talked casually as they waited, in spite of the mounting tension. Douglas in particular was so eager to capture this particular animal that he was filled with suspense. Since the lizards appeared to be insensitive to noise, the party talked at will. However, the talk was much subdued until an enormous reddish-black centipede crawled into their dark hiding place. Then for a moment the excitement within the four walls of the gloomy boma was intense. One of the Malays soon succeeded in slicing the beast in two with his parang. After that, the occupants didn't feel like stretching themselves out and making themselves comfortable. This was just as well, for the darkness seemed to attract scorpions, and one of them soon made his appearance. He was dealt with by the Malays, who cut off his stinger and then played with him, allowing him to run crab fashion from hand to hand as an entertaining distraction.

By this time the members of the party were beginning to be very uncomfortable in their restricted quarters, but the sun was well above the trees now and it was time for the dragon lizards to be abroad. After a while a small lizard appeared and maneuvered around the trap. He was followed by a very much larger one who immediately entered the trap and tried to drag the whole boar away. But the razorback had been carefully lashed in place and could not be budged. Presently Douglas saw the large lizard look up, then turn and flee into the jungle as if the very devil were after him.

"I think the big one is coming!" he exclaimed.

Then the party waited at the highest pitch for a long time without seeing or hearing anything. Suddenly one of the Malays made a strange sound. Then he looked around at the others and seemed to be very excited. "*Boeja darat!*" he said. "Land crocodile." Defosse moved toward him and peeped through the back of the boma; he gasped in surprise. Here, in truth, *was* a dragon, a living remnant of the monster lizards of the Pleistocene, much smaller to be sure, but still a remnant.

Both black eyes were fixed on the boma. Defosse didn't dare move, and after his electrifying appeal, no one else did either. Now the dragon started forward again, headed right for the boma. The Malay who had first seen him was watching carefully, and he shrank back from the small opening. Douglas could see the ugly monster very well. His color was green-black. His bony armor was scarred and blistered. His eyes, deep set in their sockets, looked out on the world from underneath overhanging brows. Defosse waited with the calm of a seasoned hunter, without saying a word. Babs was speechless. Now the creature's footsteps were plainly audible. He passed right by one side of the boma. Douglas could have reached out and touched him with his hand, and he had the tingling feeling of actually having a dragon walk by within a yard of where he crouched. All of them were rather nervous, and Defosse kept warning them to keep still.

A half hour of agony followed after the dragon had passed by the boma. He seemed to be wary of the trap and instinctively suspicious. He would walk up to the opening and almost put his head into the noose, but never quite far enough. Then he would inspect everything very closely, his snaky tongue in constant motion, while Douglas' hand was ever ready to jerk the cord. Always, just as Douglas expected him to take the fatal step, the lizard would turn abruptly and walk away again, then sit motionless, looking into the surrounding jungle for minutes at a time. This happened over and over again. Everyone's nerves were in a terrible state, for they all so longed to catch this monster that the suspense was almost unendurable.

At that moment, a vague hum was heard in the distance. It grew louder and louder and then, in a great roar, something seemed to be descending upon them, as if an airplane were diving with the engine full on. But it passed over the boma. It was the sound of millions of wings; a great swarm of bees was moving through the jungle, darkening the sky above the waiting party. The sound died away again into a barely audible mysterious hum, and after that, Douglas was conscious of a deathly silence except for a slight rustle of leaves. The big lizard still remained immovable, as though fascinated by a sound he perhaps did not even notice. Then suddenly it happened!

The lizard walked quickly up to the opening, stepped through the noose and seized the bait! Douglas jerked the release and it went off! The dragon surely received the surprise of his life for in a fraction of a second, he found himself sailing into the air. At the same moment there was a terrible cracking, and as the beast, who had been literally thrown into the air, fell again, the rope tightened and the spring pole cracked again and bent at the crack, so that the prize, instead of being suspended in midair, was on the ground tugging at the tether which held him firmly in the middle, just behind the forelegs. Then as the hunters ran out to surround him the ugly brute began vomiting. The Malays didn't dare go within yards of the captive, so Defosse prepared for action. He had been practicing with the lasso for just such an emergency, and now he stepped into the ring to meet the dragon. They made a strange pair, Douglas thought, the old hunter and his grim antagonist who, by this time, had lashed himself into a frightful rage, the foam literally dripping from his jaws. While not technically poisonous, the dragon lizard was so filthy a creature, his jaws and teeth so steeped in carrion, that a wound from him would no doubt be as deadly as that of a poisonous snake; serious and possibly fatal infection would be bound to result. Douglas knew that Defosse was well versed in the matter of capturing animals alive, but this raging monster was something quite new to him. However, Defosse was careful. He took no unnecessary chances. When his first throw missed, he recoiled his rope as methodically as if he were practicing on a tent peg in camp. The lizard was clawing frantically to get away. Then Defosse stepped up quite close behind him and roped him about the neck. The end of the rope was made fast to a tree. Another rope around the tail, to prevent that weapon from doing damage, did the trick. Now the Malays stepped forward with a long pole, hog-tied the lizard, and lashed him to the bamboo. Then the excited party started back to camp with half a dozen strong Malays carrying the dragon.

Douglas was jubilant. The primary objective of the expedition had been accomplished. He had dead specimens enough, and now there was this magnificent, if hideous, creature to take home alive!

Once in camp they thrust the lizard into the big cage, a strong wooden framework covered with the heaviest steel mesh available in Batavia. As he was slowly introduced at one end of the oblong, boxlike cage, the thongs that held him were cut one by one. When he felt himself free to move again within the four walls, he lashed himself into another magnificent fury. Then he began vomiting, and the stench was so appalling they left him there, a king deposed.

That evening by the fire, Douglas felt infinitely delighted with the capture, and yet he could not but feel a spark of remorse as he looked around the magnificent country, silvered in the moonlight. After all, this was the domain of the dragon; here he had ruled supreme and there was nothing but man to threaten him. Man had rarely come here. Had it not been for this museum expedition, the dragon lizards might have continued to dominate Komodo for many years to come. Now this would no doubt be changed. It was not a happy thought for one who deeply revered all of life.

10

Departure

Strange dreams disturbed Douglas' sleep that night — black, armored bodies slithering through grass, trapped animals with thrashing tails, and once the bleak vision of a square room with bars on the window, and no door, no door at all! A horror and despair seized on him, for he was in that room with no way out, and he didn't know why, or for how long. This dream woke him up with a lunge and a moment's confusion. Then he lay there vastly relieved that it was a dream, and watched the flickering of the night fire on the palm thatch, while he thought of the past, the present, and the future. All was silent except for the sound of the wind, the night voices of the jungle, and a faint murmur from the natives' huts as if a man talked in his sleep.

Morning came, rosy, fresh, cold but warming fast with the sun. As soon as Douglas was up he went to see how the new prize was coming along.

He found the cage empty.

The heavy steel mesh had been ripped asunder at the square top of the cage, pushed aside, and the great dragon was gone. The numbing shock was almost too much. Oh no! Douglas cried to himself. The crowning climax of the expedition lost! Not even any pictures made yet — he had been so sure of the capture and of the unlimited time ahead for photographing and observing him. They would never see that lizard again. He must be by now in the furthermost, highest reaches of the island, or more likely, deep underground in some cave. Douglas remembered every aspect of the battle with the scarred old king; he remembered the duel between Defosse and the lizard, of how the hunter had risked serious injury to take the dragon alive. Now, through miscalculation, the prize was lost. But who would have thought the beast would have strength enough to rip that heavy steel mesh?

He hated to take the news back to the others. Babs was dismayed when she heard; Dunn looked stricken; but Defosse merely looked thoughtful, shrugged his shoulders and said, "So it goes. Maybe we can find another one, even bigger."

But they couldn't. They sought and watched during the next few days, but they saw no more of the king of Komodo, or of any other lizard that came close to matching him in size. Then the day came when they must break camp and move back to the beach, from there to board the SS *Dog*, for the trip back home. As the Malays gathered up their loads, Douglas stood apart, looked over the scene, and thought about the weeks just passed. One thing was certain — the expedition was a success. He had twelve excellent dead specimens of the *Varanus komodoensis*, and two live adult lizards waiting for him in the camp below. The dragon did exist. His party was the first group of scientists to find him, study him, and catch him alive. Dunn's collection of reptiles and insects was a most significant and valuable one. The time and the money had been well spent. He hated the thought of leaving behind the largest lizard of all, but he realized that the purposes of science were fully as well attained by the smaller specimens. The important thing was knowledge. The great dragon alive in the Bronx Zoo might have increased popular excitement about Komodo, but its presence actually would have added little real value to the expedition's findings. They already were solid. Science knew more at this moment about the world than it had when he and his companions first approached the island through the boiling purple seas.

Defosse had gone down earlier; now he led up the mountain the remaining Malays from the base camp as

well as some members of the *Dog's* crew. Equipment of
little value was simply left, and the remaining material
made up not-too-heavy loads for the two dozen men to
carry. The camp itself was left standing. As the party
filed over the first rise of land, Douglas went last. He
paused a moment on the ridge and looked back at the
circle of huts in the rippling, waving sea of golden grass.
The sun glinted from the water hole, the mimosa trees
added their graceful designs, and in the distance the Prehistoric Wood made a dark shadow on the land. Douglas felt sad. One more beautiful wilderness spot lived in,
known, loved. Would he ever see it again?

He gave the place the salute of sadness and turned
away.

The trip down was bad enough, but they took their
time and, no doubt hardened by the active life of the
past weeks, even Babs had reserves of energy when they
reached the beach. She wiped her streaming face and
suggested to Douglas that they take a swim.

They rowed out to a small coral island in the bay.
Then they plunged into the water, which was cool and
delicious. The beach of red sand slipped off into green
water where live coral grew. Beyond that it dropped
away into the deep blue of many fathoms. Thousands
of fish swam in and out among the fantastic rainbow-
colored formations. A large black fin sailed by over the

still waters. Then there was a commotion. Douglas and Babs ran ashore, and small fish jumped in every direction. The black fin disappeared. A reddish light slanted across the bay and struck the beach of red sand. They went into the water again, noting that their little coral island was like a spot of fire in an ocean of greens and blues. They kept close to its shore, diving among the beautiful growths of coral.

When they came ashore to dress, they saw clouds of smoke issuing from the smokestack of the SS *Dog*. Their ship was getting up steam. It was time to go.

The jagged outlines of Komodo's peaks were still in sight when sunset flared and purple dusk arrived, with night at last blotting out the island that now would always mean so much to Douglas Burden. He stood on the *Dog*'s fantail, looking astern to the faint blur of darker dark down near the horizon while the first stars came out. He was sad, and yet happy at the same time. Sad because he was leaving this beautiful and exciting place, and the chances were that he would never return.

But so many other things lay ahead to be done in life.

Index

The Author

The graduate of the Naval Academy, John Clagett followed duty as a lieutenant commander during World War II with three years' service in the United States Embassy in Oslo, Norway. When he returned to America, he attended Yale University and received a Ph.D. in American Studies. Now an associate professor of English at Middlebury College, Mr. Clagett has published a number of novels. His short stories have appeared in *The Saturday Evening Post, Collier's,* and *Blue Book.*

Mr. Clagett, his wife, and their two daughters live in Vermont.